V. P. Dona

THE
INFIRMITIES
OF
GENIUS

THE
INFIRMITIES
OF
GENIUS

by

W. R. BETT

We are indebted to the National Portrait Gallery
for permission to reproduce the illustration facing
page 88.

CHRISTOPHER JOHNSON

LONDON

By the Same Author

OSLER: THE MAN AND THE LEGEND

THE SHORT-LIVED SPRING: POEMS

A SHORT HISTORY OF SOME COMMON DISEASES

(Editor)

PRINTED AND MADE IN GREAT BRITAIN BY
PAGE BROS. (NORWICH) LTD.

FOR CHRISTOPHER JOHNSON PUBLISHERS LTD.
11/14 STANHOPE MEWS WEST, LONDON, S.W.7.

First Published 1952

CONTENTS

To

Walter de la Mare

with admiration, affection, and gratitude for many
delightful and inspiriting conversations and many
delightful and inspiriting letters

'As a memory stealing out of the mind's slumber,
A memory floating up from a dark water,
Can be more beautiful than the thing remembered.'

Laurence Binyon

LIST OF ILLUSTRATIONS

PREFACE

THE medical diagnosis of a man long dead is always difficult, so that of necessity there will be a large speculative element in these essays of mine. My excuse for presenting them to the general public is my firm belief that an intimate and sympathetic knowledge of an author's medical or psychiatric case-history will enable the reader to appreciate or enjoy his works all the more.

Some of these studies are here published for the first time. Others have previously appeared as articles in *Clinical Excerpts*. They have been rewritten, with their medical 'jargon' discarded, and I am indebted to Dr F. J. Stockman, Vice-President of Winthrop-Stearns Inc. of New York City, for permission to use the idea behind them and some of their material. My thanks are also due to my secretaries, Miss Cecilia E. Holder and Mr T. H. Bishop, for their untiring and skilful help in preparing this volume for publication.

This book is almost exclusively concerned with abnormal people—with the psychopathology of genius, and on numerous occasions my friend and mentor, Mr Walter de la Mare, has posed to me the question: What is the normal man? But to this question neither he nor I could return an answer. It was he who first suggested my collecting the original articles in book form, and it is to him that the book is now appropriately dedicated—as a reward and as an affectionate tribute.

London.   W.R.B.

THOMAS CARLYLE (1795–1881)

A Victim of Dyspeptic Neurasthenia

> 'Thought, he [Dr. Cabanis] is inclined to hold, is still secreted by the brain; but then Poetry and Religion (and it is really worth knowing) are "a product of the smaller intestines"!'
>
> CARLYLE: *Critical and Miscellaneous Essays*, Vol. II, *Signs of the Times.*

A GREAT figure in English literature during a period of literary greatness, Thomas Carlyle by his majestic and often breathless language caught the ear of his age and has captured the imagination of posterity. That paradoxically the very brilliance of his style is in large measure due to its deliberate artificiality intrigues a reader with a knowledge of medicine, who attempts to diagnose in the author's jaw-twisting phrases, his tortuous parentheses, his addiction to alliterations and to capital letters, that nervous irritability to which he was a lifelong martyr.

The average layman, inclined to think of Carlyle as a breaker of images, an eccentric, grim, ill-tempered recluse, in a mood of somewhat uncritical admiration readily applies to him that undefined and indefinable term *genius*. Apart from this functional concept, there is no doubt that Carlyle *was* a genius. The greatest historian since Gibbon, his imaginative grasp of the facts of history and his gift of presenting them in thrilling language justly earn him that appellation.

How does genius fit in with what we know of his everyday life and with his medical history in particular?

Thomas Carlyle was born on December 4, 1795, at Ecclefechan, a village in Dumfriesshire. His father, who was by turn a farm servant, stonemason, and farmer, was a man endowed with shrewd ambitions and strong moral convictions. Puritanical and intolerant of contradiction, he lacked the saving grace of humour so richly possessed by his second wife.

All his life the son was devotedly attached to his mother. The two were almost like lovers, and there is much to suggest that Carlyle suffered from an Oedipus complex. He once dreamed that he had been sent by his mother to attend his father's funeral, and on another occasion he uttered words peculiar in significance, when commenting to his wife on his restlessness in London:—

'Such children who long now for this, now for that, are not well off anywhere. The thing they so want, I suppose, is to get to sleep well on their mother's bosom.'

As a child Carlyle was sensitive and shrinking, yet inclined to be moody and quick-tempered. In view of the intensity with which he attacked the herd instinct in his writings, it is interesting to recall that he complained bitterly of persecution at the hands of his schoolfellows. 'Tom the Tearful' he was called during his schooldays— a period which he described as the most unhappy in his life, though he received an excellent education for one of his social status. As he approached puberty he was constantly assailed by neurasthenia which apparently originated in his stomach and liver. As a student at Edinburgh University (1809–14) he was regarded as sarcastic and 'splenetic'. Though he lacked grievously in the social graces, he greatly impressed his fellows with his ability to learn, mastering mathematics, acquiring several languages, and adding a smattering of science to his store of knowledge.

Having no desire to pursue any particular career, he flirted for a time with the law, taught mathematics, and wrote for magazines and dictionaries. In the end he gave himself to literature and during his long life played the rôles of scholar, thinker, prophet, reformer, and invalid. Long and weary years were to pass before he succeeded in surprising, inspiring, and holding his generation— years of poverty, privation, and tremendous work. By then his hair was grey, and the iron had entered into his soul.

The Tragedy of Marriage

In 1826 Carlyle married the beautiful, blackhaired Jane Welsh with the soft, mocking eyes and the biting tongue. They had much, perhaps too much, in common. Both suffered the torment of persistent insomnia. Both were morbidly sensitive to noise. Alike in their attitude to their fellow beings, whom they were only too ready to dismiss as bores or fools, both possessed remarkable powers of expression.

Their marriage was not so much unhappy as joyless. Only child of a 'very self-possessed' and 'usually strangely silent' medical practitioner, Jane had inherited some of the qualities of her father's ancestor, formidable John Knox, and from her mother's side chronic nervous instability. Sick headaches which she described as bilious attacks, alternated with severe bouts of influenza, leaving neuralgia and depression in their wake. As the years went by she grew into a highly neurotic woman. In 1863 she lost the use of her left arm and hand ('neuralgic rheumatism'); two years later the other arm was affected, while paralysis of the muscles of the jaws made speaking difficult and caused acute misery. The patient sought relief by taking opium, but this served only to deepen her melancholia and to intensify her morbid suspicions.

Like her husband, Jane Carlyle was a bundle of contradictions. Her vivacity, charm, and generosity would make her a delightful companion to those whom she liked, but with others she could be cynical in the extreme and most provoking. The two undoubtedly irritated each other, but though their married life appears to have been devoid of many of the outward signs of love, their relations were tolerably friendly. They did not escape the malice of gossiping tongues, and the rumours and speculations of the most intimate nature which had long been current, seemed to find some justification when Froude first suggested the possibility of Carlyle's impotence.

James Anthony Froude, the historian, was a close friend

of Carlyle, and as his biographer and literary executor he thought fit to publish certain details of the intimacies and infirmities under which this genius laboured. The sincerity of his motives cannot be doubted, but like many who pursue what they consider to be the path of duty he brought down upon himself an avalanche of indignation and abuse. He was accused of ill-natured indiscretion, and even to-day people are shocked when they read such revelations. Poor Froude was bewildered, finding himself condemned for indelicacy when all the time he had been actuated by respect for historical accuracy. Had he not regarded it as his solemn duty to present all the facts as he knew them about his late friend that posterity might not be led astray in their interpretation of his character?

Carlyle's alleged impotence is something which can neither be proved nor disproved, though some internal evidence in the lives and writings of both husband and wife tends to make the suggestion not merely frivolous or malevolent. Increasing psychological understanding of the influence of childhood environment on mental and physical health makes the gloomy married life of the Carlyles an absorbing study.

Carlyle was aware of the rumours concerning him, for he heard from a friend that the talk in the London Clubs was 'Carlyle is impotent'. He assured his informant that this was untrue. Passages in his historical work *Frederick the Great*, suggest that he brooded over this accusation when he refers to the baseless accusations concerning the sex-life of his hero, comparing those ever on the look-out for 'smut' with dogs, interested only in the 'shameful parts of the constitution'.

Jane Carlyle, as many childless women have done, found an emotional outlet for her affections by surrounding herself with a bizarre menagerie of pets such as dogs, cats, canaries, hedgehogs, and even leeches. Fond of social life, she entertained visitors and admirers in her downstairs room in the Cheyne Row house, while Thomas, secure in his sound-proof eyrie, sought to forget domestic and dyspeptic worries in the solace of work. They occupied separate bedrooms.

Besides being an opium addict, Jane Carlyle smoked cigarettes—a habit which at that time exposed her to charges of unladylike behaviour. On April 21, 1866, she died of a heart attack while being driven in her brougham in Hyde Park. Carlyle was in Dumfries at the time. As they had been separated in life by an insurmountable, though indefinable, barrier, so when death came, they were far apart.

The Invalid

From early childhood Carlyle suffered from dyspepsia, which he likened to 'a rat gnawing at the pit of the stomach'. His years at Edinburgh University were marred by insomnia and its attendant troubles; he was, as he described it, 'a prey to nameless struggles and miseries, which have yet a kind of horror in them to my thoughts, three weeks without any kind of sleep, from impossibility to be free from noise'. The wretched man tried a host of remedies for the disabling pain which made life a burden. When he was twenty-eight he forsook his beloved tobacco on the advice of a 'long hairy-eared jackass' of a doctor, who prescribed mercury. 'There is mercurial powder in me, and a gnawing pain over all the organs of digestion, especially in the pit and left side of the stomach.'

As a writer Carlyle is remarkable for his powers of vivid and picturesque description, but nowhere did he use those powers more successfully than in recording his infirmities and the physical and mental sufferings he endured. A manufacturer of chemicals in Birmingham and, ironically, himself a victim of dyspepsia, who was known as 'Stomach curer Badams', persuaded him to live under his roof while undergoing a course of treatment. His methods ('regimen and exercises are his specifics, assisted by as little gentlest medicine as possible') failed, however, to effect the slightest improvement.

'I have been bephysicked and bedrugged', the patient wrote. 'I have swallowed about two stouppels of castor oil since I came hither; unless I dose myself with that oil of sorrow I cannot get along at all.' Carlyle's excessive intro-spection caused him to exaggerate all the ailments of body and mind. As far as his health was concerned he lacked any reticence, introducing the subject in his correspondence and in conversation—in season and out of season, with the result that we know more of his day-to-day medical history than of that of most famous men. Obsessed as he was with these ugly details and possessed of a pen skilled in the art of creating telling word-pictures, he left many a description which is as fascinating as it is revealing.

The catalogue of gloom began in childhood. It con-tinued into old age. At the age of thirty-one he was 'sick with sleeplessness, nervous, bilious, splenetic, and all the rest of it'. When he was forty he confessed: 'it is strange how one gets habituated to sickness. . . . I fight with dullness and bile in the forenoons as of old'. Two years later he complained: 'I was wasted and fretted to a thread. My tongue, let me drink as I would, continued as dry as charcoal.' In vain did he try changing the dinner hour to the middle of the day; his 'biliousness' refused to desert him.

In August, 1851, Carlyle and his wife went to Malvern, where they stayed as the guests of Dr. James Manby Gully. Son of a Jamaica coffee planter, this physician enjoyed considerable reputation as a practitioner of hydropathy (the 'water cure'). In Charles Reade's *It is Never Too Late to Mend*, 'Dr. Gullson' is meant as a portrait of Dr. Gully, who also played a leading rôle in a drama of real life. This was the Bravo case which concerned the death of Charles Bravo, a barrister, suspected of having poisoned his wife, with whom Gully had been on terms of intimacy. The doctor's professional reputation suffered grievously, and his name was erased from the medical societies. Gully's water cure availed nothing in Carlyle's case. 'The bathing, packing, drinking proved useless—worse than useless', only confirming the patient in his opinion that medical advice was worthless. 'Of all the sons of Adam, men of medicine are the most unprofitable.'

Two of Carlyle's medical advisers were eminent men, whose names are remembered in history. Sir Richard Quain, Bart., F.R.S., President of the General Medical Council, Physician Extraordinary to Queen Victoria, and editor of one of the most successful medical books ever published—Quain's *Dictionary of Medicine*, attended both Thomas and Jane Carlyle and signed the latter's death certificate. Thomas's 'wretched dyspepsia' in his opinion was fully accounted for by his excessive fondness for very nasty gingerbread. The only remedy he could ever get him to take was grey powder (mercury with chalk).

In his last illness Carlyle was in the care of a brother Scot, Thomas John Maclagan, Doctor of Medicine of Edinburgh University, who lives in the Annals of Medicine as a pioneer in treating rheumatic fever with salicylates. This was a revolutionary advance in the treatment of a disease which had been the despair of generations of doctors.

The nature of the dyspepsia which cast Carlyle for so long into the 'Slough of Despond' cannot be diagnosed with accuracy. He himself stated repeatedly that his sufferings were real and acute, blaming the stomach and liver. It is interesting to note, however, that the pains which he described so eloquently could never be precisely localized to any one specific organ in the body. This would tend to exclude the probability of organic disease being present, and there is certainly no evidence of ulcer of the stomach or duodenum. According to his biographer Froude, Carlyle's health was always singularly robust, and we are told that he was in the habit of going out-of-doors in inclement weather, completely indifferent to rain or cold.

With advancing years the symptoms which had caused him so much distress diminished considerably in their intensity. The distinguished Philadelphia eye specialist and lexicographer, George Milbry Gould, made out a good case for the belief that those symptoms were due to eye-strain caused by astigmatism. He quoted extracts from

Carlyle's writings to support his theory, showing that his complaints were more pronounced when he did much reading and writing—intellectual activity left him quite unfatigued—and that they diminished when he was able to rest his eyes. Gould laid particular stress on the fact that cessation of symptoms came precisely at the time when the accommodating function of the eye was paralysed by old age.

In 1868, when he was in his seventy-fourth year, Carlyle fell from his horse and now gave up riding. He had taken up this exercise in 1839, when a certain gentleman, distressed by his recitals of dyspepsia and constipation, had made him a present of a horse. Around 1870 tremulousness and twitching developed in his right hand, making writing impossible. It is amusing to find that dictation never appealed to him, because it resulted in 'diluted moonshine'.

Eleven sad and lonely years had to pass before Death, coming as a friend, knocked at his door on February 5, 1881. Most of his friends had gone before him into the night, which he knew awaited him also and to which he knew there was no morning. Unable to obtain an answer from reason, he had always sternly refused to seek it in any form of superstition.

The Hero

In the intimacies of his writings Carlyle invited the whole world behind the scenes, with the inevitable consequence that the great hero-worshipper himself has so little of the heroic about him. Let us, however, recall his many virtues. A man of enormous industry, of fierce independence, of transparent honesty. Thrifty in his own person and with his Jeannie, yet most generous in unobtrusive benefactions.

His portraits have immortalized Carlyle as a man of singular melancholy, but this is only half of the truth, for he had his moods of gaiety. Those listening to his flights

of rhetoric were sometimes surprised to hear him ending
with a shriek of laughter. In the fine portrait by Millais
in the National Portrait Gallery the sadness of his expression is relieved by the unmistakable kindness lurking in the
eyes, which regard one with so level and direct a gaze.

It is notoriously fruitless, yet fascinating, to consider the
'ifs' and 'buts', so let us try to picture to what extent
better health would have affected Carlyle's life and work.
Had his childhood been passed in a happier environment,
would he have been much different? If he had held his
father in less 'fearful fascination'; if his home had known
more of the warmth of fun and laughter, would he not
have warmed to his fellows? Would he not have been more
tolerant of human frailties? Had his married life turned out
differently, would he not have been free from the doubts
and the fears, the vexations, the self-reproaches, the heart-
searchings that tore at him so relentlessly all the days of
his life? Whether his marriage was unhappy because of
the impotence of the one partner or the sterility of the
other we may never know. We can but speculate whether
a wife less like himself in emotional make-up might have
helped him to face life without so much nervous strain. It
is possible that a woman less intellectually endowed might
have succeeded in persuading him to take life less seriously.
It is possible, too, that had he married some one who
'mothered' him, his chronic restlessness might have been
stilled or turned into other channels.

One is tempted, also, to wonder how he might have
fared with Margaret Gordon for a wife. He met this clever,
attractive young woman with the blue eyes and the yellow
hair in Kirkcaldy, and she once gave him this advice:
'Cultivate the milder dispositions of your heart. Subdue
the more extravagant visions of your brain. Genius will
render you great. May virtue render you beloved. Remove
the awful distance between you and ordinary men, and by
kind and gentle manners, deal kindly with their inferiority,
and be convinced they will respect you as much and like
you more.'

Most intriguing of all is the question: had Carlyle been

a normally happy and contented man would his genius have found expression in the same intellectual media as those in which his fame is in perpetuity enshrined? Would he, indeed, have been a genius at all? Endow a Beethoven, a Baudelaire, or a Gauguin with perfect health of mind and body, what would be the effect upon their creative powers? In other words, to what extent is a man of genius conditioned by what may be described as the accident of his body? If Carlyle, the cautious, frugal eater, had been one of those ordinary people who can with impunity eat as and when they like, with never a twinge to remind them of their indiscretion, would he have passed the same judgements, would he have dipped his pen so often in vitriol and gall to pronounce them? The psychopath notoriously suffers from his lack of stability and from the sense of inferiority which this engenders. But it is this very handicap which is a spur to intellectual creative endeavour and also gives a man increased insight into the infirmities of others.

The Man of Letters

At the early age of nineteen Carlyle had confessed his ambition: 'Think not that I am careless of literary fame. . . . Heaven knows that ever since I have been able to form a wish, the wish of being known has been the foremost.'

By that time he was already a victim of dyspeptic neurasthenia which left its impress on his every thought, mood, and word. Had he possessed rude health, this ambition of his would have been less urgent in its nagging, and the recognition for which he was to wait so long would have seemed a matter of less moment. He was doomed to go through life under the constant curse of hypersensitiveness. Every situation, every disappointment, every misunderstanding, every doubt, every trifling upset assumed in his eyes an exaggerated, and at times a grotesque, importance, wracking him in a manner which those of tougher fibre could scarcely be expected to comprehend.

When his abandonment of the old orthodoxy seemed to leave no alternative but materialism, he at first recoiled in horror, and the conflict tore his soul. 'Three weeks of total sleeplessness' had to be endured before his mental agony was brought to an end by the crisis which culminated in his 'spiritual new birth'. In his misery he felt sympathetic towards the lower classes whose sad state inspired him to write *Signs of the Times* (1829), a work in which he dwelt on the decline of political thought and the prostitution of government to self-interest.

In *The State of German Literature* (1827) he dealt with the German philosopher, Johann Gottlieb Fichte's theory of a 'Divine Idea' pervading the Universe. In expressing the view that 'Literary men are the appointed interpreters of this Divine Idea', Carlyle provided the key to much of his later writing, for it was as an interpreter that he was most influenced by his wretched physical condition. As a historian he was painstaking and scrupulously honest, but the dyspepsia and insomnia which brought irritability in their train cast their shadow over many of his pages. Thus in *Latter-Day Pamphlets* democracy had become the foolish whose 'everlasting privilege' it is to be governed by the wise. His constant reiteration of the 'hero' theme was largely an expression of his impatience with those about him. In the querulousness of the chronic dyspeptic, he could see no future for man or for institutions except under the leadership of the Hero, the *König*, the God. In *The Letters and Speeches of Oliver Cromwell*, in *Frederick the Great*, and in *On Heroes, Hero-Worship, and the Heroic in History*, he insisted on the principle of absolutism. Even in *The French Revolution* he was less concerned with the theme of justice for the oppressed people than with the vindication of the superman, the leader of the people.

Carlyle's literary style suffered from one fault in particular—the straining for effect. His contemporaries did not always appreciate the bizarre, 'barbarous', and noisy words which he employed. Brooding over the picture he wished to create, this intellectual giant would work himself up to a white heat of passion, using strong expressions and investing each sentence, each word, with the maximum of emphasis, as though thus only could he obtain relief from his nervous irritability. His conscientiousness in approaching a problem in history, added to the burning desire to make his words live, made writing a fearsome task. When engaged on *The French Revolution*, he wrote: 'After two weeks of blotching and blaring I have produced two clean pages.' When the book was completed after three years of hard work he declared: 'You have not had for a hundred years any book that comes more direct and flaming from the heart of a living man.'

In the ultimate analysis, the final impression left on the mind by Carlyle's writings is one of endless struggle, of conflict unresolved and unresolvable. But is this not what one after all expects?

In his interpretations of history and in his method of presentation, Thomas Carlyle, like any creative artist, was merely trying to express himself, was trying to interpret his own experiences. Had he been different, so would have been his work. When genius conforms to rule, then will it cease to be genius.

PERCY BYSSHE SHELLEY (1792–1822)

Neurosis and Genius

> 'Most wretched men
> Are cradled into poetry by wrong:
> They learn in suffering what they
> teach in song.'
>
> SHELLEY: *Julian and Maddalo.*

ONE hundred and thirty years have passed since Shelley's mortal remains were burned on the seashore, in accordance with the tradition of the ancient Greeks. His passionate life is spent, his revolutionary theories are dead, his perversities are forgotten. Only his poetry endures, for it represents the eternal spirit of youth, the glory and the hurt of life, the gossamer fabric of a dream. Shelley's productiveness during the short years that were allowed to his genius to flower remains one of the marvels of literary achievement. His health was poor, but in describing his life as 'a series of illness' he showed the exaggeration of the neurotic.

The Brief Flower of Youth

The eldest son of Sir Timothy Shelley, Bart., Percy Bysshe Shelley was born at Field Place, Warnham, near Horsham, on August 4, 1792. In view of his subsequent revolutionary sympathies, it is interesting to note that he first saw the light but a few days before the overthrow of the French monarchy. An arrestingly handsome boy, he was tall and delicately built, with exquisitely shaped hands and feet, a girlish throat, and dark brown curling hair, as fine as spun silk. His eyes were deep-blue, large, and luminous. For all their abruptness his movements were articulate with grace. His voice was low and hauntingly

23

soft, yet capable of peals of fiendish laughter. In him were combined seemingly opposite qualities: sensitive, shrinking, and affectionate, he could at the same time be mischievous, hot tempered, and rebellious.

At home he was the idol of his four younger sisters, for his gift for telling weird and horrible tales of phantoms and apparitions and his ability to perform elementary but spectacular experiments in chemistry and electricity made him a hero of almost supernatural powers. At Sion House Academy, Brentford, persecution at the hands of his schoolfellows led to his lifelong abhorrence of oppression and the awakening of the spirit of revolt within him. It is recorded that he had at least one attack of sleepwalking while at school. Equally legendary fits followed later.

Shelley's experiences at Eton were a repetition of those at Sion House. Many legends abound concerning his scandalous love of books, his equally scandalous devotion to poetry, his contempt for authority, his burning down an old willow with a burning-glass, his anti-religious utterances. 'Mad Shelley', 'Shelley the Atheist', appeared to have been as unpopular as he was unhappy. Driven to despair by unrequited love, he once took some arsenic, and ever after attributed his chronic ill-health to this youthful indiscretion. Like so many other 'confessions' from the imaginative lips of the poet, this early one also should be accepted with scepticism. Among Shelley's happiest recollections of Eton was a queer old man, James Lind, M.D., Physician to the Royal Household at Windsor, of whom he said: 'I owe to that man far, ah! far more than I owe to my father; he loved me, and I shall never forget our long talks, when he breathed the spirit of the kindest tolerance, and the purest wisdom.' It was from Lind that the boy acquired a veritable passion for chemistry and black magic. It is said that when his brain was affected by a 'fever', Lind's prompt cure prevented his father from consigning him to a private asylum. The physician is immortalized in *Laon and Cythna* (*The Revolt of Islam*) as the old hermit, while in the fragment *Prince Athanase* he is featured as Zonoras.

Almost as soon as he left Eton, Shelley became enamoured of, and engaged to, his cousin, the vivacious and charming Harriet Grove. When the girl in due course changed her mind, her fickleness precipitated in her passionate admirer a nervous crisis, characterized by attacks of giddiness. A more prosaic report has it that these were caused by a mild attack of typhus fever.

At University College, Oxford, Shelley's eccentric behaviour and still more eccentric attire made him a conspicuous figure. He wore a blue jacket with glistening steel buttons and Byronic collar, and wore his wavy hair long. His reading of Pliny had given him a leaning towards pantheism, under which influence he wrote and said things which he, as well as some of his critics, mistook for atheism.

The Necessity of Atheism

Shelley's pamphlet *The Necessity of Atheism*, written in the form of a geometric theorem to prove the impossibility of the existence of God, and ending *Q.E.D.*, was responsible for his expulsion from the University, in company with his intimate friend, Thomas Jefferson Hogg.

In disgrace after being sent down, Shelley took lodgings in London, at 15, Poland Street, and attended the lectures on anatomy of the celebrated John Abernethy at St. Bartholomew's Hospital with a view to taking up medicine. Medicine had a great attraction for the Shelley family. The poet's cousin, Charles Grove, was a medical student, his great grandfather had practised as a quack doctor in America, and his grandfather, the eccentric Sir Bysshe, was at one time associated with that prince of charlatans, James Graham, proprietor of the 'Temple of Health'.

The abrupt termination of his university career cannot be said to have seriously affected Shelley's future. His life during the next few years was hectic, but despite all its vicissitudes, it was one of great mental development. The most immediate and most potent influence on his mind was his unfortunate marriage with Harriet West-brook.

The Gravest Mistake of his Life

Daughter of a retired tavern-keeper, Harriet Westbrook was a fellow-pupil of Shelley's sisters at Mrs. Fenning's Academy for Young Ladies on Clapham Common. Her charm instantly entered the poet's soul. Whether Shelley was ever profoundly in love with this adoring and adorable girl of sixteen is conjectural. She was certainly attractive to look at with her light chestnut hair, her complexion of milk and roses, her eyes bright with happiness. Dressed with exquisite neatness, she had a sweet voice and a cheerful and affectionate nature. When Harriet's friendship with an atheist threatened her with expulsion from school, her penniless, homeless, jobless, and creedless hero, moved by foolish compassion and mistaken chivalry, committed the gravest mistake of his life, promising to 'unite his fate' with a mere child who was prepared to become his mistress. In the year of the great comet, foreshadowing the fire of Moscow, the two lovers eloped. Elopement, like doctoring, was a tradition in the Shelley family. Sir Bysshe had eloped with both his wives, and two daughters followed in their father's footsteps. Shelley and Harriet fled to Edinburgh, where on August 28, 1811, they became man and wife in the sight of the law.

His broken engagement to Harriet Grove to Shelley had been in the nature of a tragedy, which he dramatized to the utmost, avowing that all that remained for him in life was to bring happiness to others. It was this attitude of mind which led to his impulsive marriage with Harriet Westbrook. Future events were to show that his quixotic action, far from bringing happiness to his wife, was to cause both acute anguish of soul and was to end in tragedy.

In 1813 Shelley and Harriet travelled to London, where their daughter Ianthe was born. It was not long, however, before through radical incompatibility of temperament

26

they became estranged. Harriet who had been content to abide by her husband's decisions and who found her happiness in his company and in listening to his every word, waxed proud, rebellious, and cold. When Shelley met Mary Wollstonecraft Godwin, daughter of the philosopher William Godwin, he soon fell violently in love with the pale pure face, the golden hair, and the nut-brown eyes of this highly intelligent girl of sixteen. Harriet was in the fourth month of her second pregnancy when her husband declared his intention of eloping with Mary, and when she refused to agree to a separation he carelessly suggested that the three should live together under one roof, Mary as his wife and Harriet as a sister.

Poor Harriet, betrayed by life, fated to see her husband live with another girl and abandoning hope of winnowing any fragments of conjugal happiness, fell upon evil days. Even at this distance of time her story is unutterably poignant, its all-too brief joy so quickly blotted out by the remorseless shadow of destiny. How reminiscent of the quietly sinister, inevitable unfolding of a Greek tragedy. The end of her life remains shrouded in mystery. Assuming the name of Harriet Smith, for a brief period she took lodgings at 7, Elizabeth Street, Hans Place, but in November, 1816, she left in despair and degradation— mistress of a nameless man who had deserted her. On December 10th her body, far advanced in pregnancy, was found in the Serpentine Lake. She had been dead some three weeks. A fortnight after her remains had been recovered from the waters of death, Shelley and Mary Godwin were united in unholy matrimony.

In 1813 Shelley began to suffer from acute pain in his chest, which threw him into convulsions, and for the relief of which he made liberal use of laudanum. He would carry the bottle in his hand, drinking from it freely as the pain came on. About this time he excused his avidity for rushing into print by saying that his physical constitution did not hold out hopes of a long life. While on a visit to Dublin, he placed himself on a vegetarian diet, though weakness following the seasickness he experienced on his return voyage, forced him to return to more substantial fare.

Like his brother-poet Byron, he seriously undermined his health by injudicious dieting. In March, 1812, Harriet wrote: 'We have forsworn meat, and adopted the Pythagorean system. About a fortnight has elapsed since the change, and we do not find ourselves any the worse for it. . . . We are delighted with it, and think it the best thing in the world.' Shelley himself went even further in praise of vegetarianism, stating in the notes to *Queen Mab:* 'There is no disease, bodily or mental, which adoption of vegetable diet and pure water has not infallibly mitigated.'

The Invalid

Shelley's morbid hypersensitiveness—a genuine hypochondriasis which magnified beyond recognition his existing disorders and lent verisimilitude to those which existed only in his imagination—makes it difficult to diagnose with accuracy the nature of the ailment which kept him in a state of chronic invalidism. A peculiar instance of the morbid fear of contracting disease which possessed him has been recorded. After a journey in a crowded stage-coach, when he had sat opposite an old woman with very fat legs, he became convinced that he was afflicted with elephantiasis, and nothing would shake his belief that he had caught the disease from her. According to his friend Thomas Love Peacock, 'He used to draw the skin of his own hand, arms and neck very tight, and if he discovered any deviation, he would seize the person next to him and endeavour by a corresponding pressure to see if any corresponding deviation existed.' Young ladies, subjected unawares to these experiments, not unnaturally found them embarrassing and could be excused if they mistook his motives. Sometimes he would twist on the floor like an eel, saying, 'I have the elephantiasis'. That he exaggerated the importance of trivial incidents we know from the fact that, if he happened to cough, he would assert that a few blood-vessels had just ruptured and that he was spitting blood.

At one time, it is true, a medical man had shared his gloomy outlook, for in the spring of 1815 Dr.Christopher Robert Pemberton pronounced him to be rapidly dying of consumption. Pemberton was Physician-Extraordinary to the King, a Fellow of the Royal Society, and a sound clinical observer. Despite his grave view of the patient's condition, however, we know from Mary Shelley that suddenly 'a complete change took place, and though through life he was a martyr to pain and debility, every symptom of pulmonary disease vanished'. Attributable in part to the open air life he led during a tour along the Devon coast and a trip on the Thames, his recovery was probably aided by his substitution of well-peppered mutton-chops for a vegetarian diet.

By June, 1817, the pain in his side had become constant, and he was terribly depressed. In September the famous surgeon and orator, Sir William Lawrence of St.Bartholomew's Hospital, advised him to submit to complete rest, with change of scene and air. On March 12, 1818, Shelley left England for ever, and for a while the more equable climate of Italy was kind to him: he grew more manly, and his chest measurements, in particular, were noticeably improved. During the few years remaining to him his genius developed to full maturity, and he wrote the greater part of the poetry which will endure for all time.

Even the sunny skies of Italy and its wealth of literary and historical delights could not banish for ever his predisposition to dwell upon his afflictions. In November, 1818, he consulted an English physician at Naples, who diagnosed his malady as liver disease for which he recommended riding and the application of caustics to the side. It was at this period that the poet wrote the despairing *Stanzas Written in Dejection Near Naples:*

> ' Alas! I have not hope nor health
> Nor peace within nor calm around.'

The shadow of death was often upon him. Early in 1819

he tried to take his life with opium. It was not his first attempt at suicide, and by no means the first time he had allowed his thoughts to dwell on the peace which comes only with death. When in Pisa, Shelley became a patient of Andrea Vaccà-Berlinghieri, professor of surgery at the University, and a scientist of international reputation, who diagnosed his complaint as kidney trouble, and persuaded him to give up taking laudanum.

As soon as the poet had abandoned laudanum, feeling the need of something to take its place, he turned to hypnotism. Having for so long looked upon himself as a consumptive, the diagnosis of kidney trouble brought new fears, and on January 2, 1821, he wrote: 'I have suffered considerably from my disease; and am already in imagination, preparing to be cut for the stone, in spite of Vacca's consolatory assurance.' In the following April his health was 'amended by the divine weather . . . but still characterized by irritability and depression.' It is noticeable that when he deserted his books for a while and took outdoor exercise there was usually an improvement in his health and spirits.

Many conflicting opinions have been expressed on the nature of Shelley's invalidism, which has been variously diagnosed as gallstone, gastric ulcer, duodenal ulcer, and epilepsy. The suggestion that the poet was an epileptic is based on reports that while at Oxford he once or twice fell into lethargic trances. In the midst of so much doubt it is impossible to venture on a firm clinical diagnosis, but one can be more confident in concluding that Shelley was largely the victim of his own powerful imagination. His physical condition was the consequence of his sedentary habits, and his neurotic tendency was responsible for magnifying the symptoms engendered by those habits. His attacks of spitting of blood were mythical, just as his elephantiasis was mythical. There was no question outside his own mind that he would ever be cut for the stone.

Shelley's radiant faith in the possibility of attaining perfection found expression, not only in attacks on institutions and prejudices, but in the supersensitiveness which made common ailments appear as grave disorders. He was courageous, but subject to mental anguish which wracked him in moments of stress. Governed by rules of his own, the world's censure never caused him to change a course of action, nor did it ever embitter him. In some ways heedless of others, he yet possessed beauty of character, unselfishness, and generosity. It was characteristic of him that the suicide of his wife Harriet filled him with regret and horror, but not with remorse. Conventions meant nothing to him, and blissfully unconscious of any wrong-doing, he felt no responsibility for the tragedy. His was that artistic temperament which constantly seeks the novelty of fresh experience and fresh adventure. Out of his numerous affairs of the heart arose his belief that love was not wholly a desire of the flesh, but rather the artistically perfect and exalted blending of the physical, the spiritual, and the intellectual. For such a love he would soar into the blue of heaven and descend into the pit of hell.

Shelley's death from drowning on July 8, 1822, in his thirtieth year, is familiar to all. It brought the end which he had often contemplated with such longing. But a few days earlier he had written to Edward John Trelawny, asking him to try to obtain for him some prussic acid or essential oil of bitter almonds. Trelawny must not think that he was bent on using it, but 'It would be a comfort to me to hold in my possession the golden key to the chamber of perpetual rest.'

To that great physician and humanist, Sir William Osler, 'a student for many years of the art and of the act of dying', Shelley's lines 'Mild was the slow necessity of death: The tranquil spirit failed beneath its grasp', was a perfect description of dying, which he was fond of quoting.

In bidding farewell, then, to Shelley, let us pass quickly from that first mood of despair:

> 'Under the obscure, cold, rotting, wormy ground!
> To see no more sweet sunshine; hear no more
> Blithe voice of living thing; muse not again
> Upon familiar thoughts. . . .'

to that final defiant note of triumph:

'The splendours of the firmament of time
May be eclipsed, but are extinguished not;
Like stars to their appointed height they climb
And death is a low mist which cannot blot
The brightness of the veil.'

CHRISTOPHER SMART (1722-71)

Insanity as a Shadow of Genius.

> 'Great wits are sure to madness near alli'd,
> And thin partitions do their bounds divide.
>
> DRYDEN: *Absalom and Achitophel.*

FROM the earliest recorded times insanity has shadowed those who have scaled the heights of Parnassus and have drunk deep of the waters of Hippocrene. Impressive in its length and distinction is the melancholy catalogue of men of literary genius who lived with madness or walked in dread of its wings brushing their mind. In Christopher Smart we find an intriguing example of one whose poetry reached supreme heights only during periods of mental derangement, most of his work before he suffered his first attack of insanity being mediocre and that written after his recovery descending to the same level.

Christopher Smart was born on April 11, 1722, at Shipbourne, near Tunbridge in Kent, son of the steward of Lord Vane's Fairlawn estates. His first schooling was received at Maidstone and at Durham Grammar School, and his holidays were frequently spent visiting Raby Castle, near Darlington—the Vane family seat. His lines *To Ethelinda* are said to have been inspired by his precocious love for Lady Anne Vane, who was even younger than he when at thirteen he persuaded her to elope with him.

His personality made so deep an impression on Henrietta, Duchess of Cleveland, that she made him an annuity of £40, which enabled him to seek admittance to Pembroke Hall, Cambridge, in 1739, where he graduated B.A. three years later. His extravagance and liking for taverns did not blind the authorities to his ability, for he was elected a Fellow of Pembroke in July, 1745, and became Praelector in Philosophy and Keeper of the Common Chest in October. When he graduated M.A. in 1747 he was already heavily in debt. 'He must necessarily be abîmé in a very short time', wrote the poet Gray in a letter, 'his Debts daily increasing. . . . His Vanity and Faculty of Lyeing, they are come to their full Maturity. All this, you see, must come to a Jayl or Bedlam.' Meanwhile Smart was passing the time by writing an extravaganza *A Trip to Cambridge, or the Grateful Fair,* which was acted in Pembroke Hall during that summer. Commenting on Smart's almost childish glee over his own farce, Gray said: 'He can't hear the Prologue without being ready to die with Laughter. He acts five parts himself, is only sorry he can't do all the rest.' If Gray at times seems to have been a little petty in his criticisms of Smart, he probably suffered from the young man's witticisms. A prim little man who took himself very seriously he 'commonly held up his gown behind him with one of his hands, at the same time cocking up his chin, and perking up his nose'. Smart's allusion to this habit was that 'Gray walked as if he had fouled his small clothes, and looked as if he smelt it'. His ability to rattle off such sallies may have been partly responsible for his undoing: a ready wit, he was invited to drink with strangers, and thus not only drank more than was good for him, but in returning their treats he ran himself hopelessly into debt.

In November, 1747, he lost his appointments and was arrested for a debt of £50. Though reappointed Praelector in 1748, in the following year he went to London, where he made a living of sorts as a journalist. In 1750 he won the Seatonian prize for sacred poetry at Cambridge, for a poem on the attributes of the Supreme Being, and with the exception of 1754, when he did not enter for it, he gained the prize every year up to 1755.

34

In November, 1753, the College authorities learned of his marriage to Anna Maria Carnan, and it was only on condition that he continued to enter for the Seatonian prize that his Fellowship was extended. His wife's widowed mother had married John Newbery, the publisher, to whom Smart had been introduced by Dr. Charles Burney. Newbery was delighted by the poet's ability to produce nonsense verse and other literary *jeux d'esprit*, which pleased the public taste. Much of Smart's work at this period was published in such ephemeral and somewhat coarse journals as *The Widwife, or Old Woman's Magazine*. His *Poems on Several Occasions*, published in 1752, were adversely criticized by the notorious 'Sir' John Hill, the hack writer, would-be-dramatist, and quack whose attempts at a stage career had ended in failure. In reply Smart wrote the satirical ode *The Hilliad*, in which he gave Hill ample cause to regret his anonymous attack. After he had resigned his Fellowship the poet's affairs went from bad to worse. His prose translation of Horace which he finished in 1756 brought him little pecuniary reward, although the booksellers did very well out of its sales.

The Wings of Insanity

In November, 1755, Smart entered into an extraordinary agreement by which he and Richard Rolt were to produce a weekly paper, *The Universal Visiter*. This contract has been the cause of much misunderstanding; Dr. Johnson and De Quincey, for example, citing it as an instance of the rapacity of booksellers. The discovery of the original contract in Reading in 1928 has shown that the terms were not unfavourable. Although the articles were to run for ninety-nine years, any of the signatories were free to drop out if the journal lost money over any six-months' period. The supposition that Smart was to write only for the journal is erroneous, he and the other signatories agreeing only that they would not assist any periodical which might compete with *The Universal Visiter*. Smart's contributions, as it happened, were few, for his mind was giving way, and his part of the bargain could not have been fulfilled had not Dr. Johnson, Garrick, and other friends rallied to his assistance. The fact that Johnson's first contributions appeared in the early numbers of *The Universal Visiter* and were written to help Smart 'secure his share of the profits of it' is an indication that the poet's mental illness began early in 1756. It has been suggested that he was in Newbery's care at his premises in St. Gregory's Parish, where St. Luke's Hospital, which he entered on May 6, 1757, was situated. He was discharged, though not recovered, on May 11, 1758.

In the following February he was 'much reduced', and Garrick put on *Merope* for his benefit, together with his farce *The Guardian*, in which he played the part of Heartly. Smart's financial condition was such that his wife and children were for some years dependent on his sister, who received them in her home in Ireland.

It was probably sometime in 1759 that Smart began to write his *Jubilate Agno*—a bizarre poem, modelled on the Psalms and on the Magnificat. In a strange blending of the beautiful with the meaningless and the irrational, the deranged poet calls on mankind, birds, beasts, fishes, and flowers to join in praising their Creator. His knowledge and love of all living creatures are among his most endearing qualities. In *The Story of a Cock and a Bull* he made a humanitarian plea for greater kindness to domestic animals.

In *Christopher Smart: A Biographical and Critical Study* by Edward G. Ainsworth and Charles E. Noyes. Columbia: University of Missouri. 1943, we have a valuable study of the poet's life and work. Noyes, to whom fell the task of completing the book after the death of Dr. Ainsworth in 1940, wrote of the *Jubilate Agno:* 'Such a work, with its passages of exotic beauty and its queer, illogical shifts, is material more fit for study by a psychoanalyst than a biographer.' Fortunately, the case of Smart has since been made the subject of an essay by a distinguished neurologist, but before quoting from this authority, there are further biographical details to consider. Noyes, by careful reading of the *Jubilate Agno*, makes out a good case for the supposition that after his release from St. Luke's Hospital, Smart was kept at home until a date shortly after August 13, 1759. In his opinion there is no proof that the poet was then confined to Bethlehem Hospital. Fanny Burney's reference to 'Bedlam' is inconclusive as that term was often applied to madhouses in general.

In 1948 Dr. W. Russell Brain contributed an illuminating article on " Christopher Smart : The Flea that became an Eagle," to the *Medical Bookman and Historian* (1948, **2,** 295–300). He has this to say of the *Jubilate Agno:* 'It shows all the features of maniacal excitement. Clearly he suffered from manic-depressive insanity or cyclothymia; a disorder characterized by recurrent attacks of depression and excitement or predominantly by one or the other.' In support of this conclusion he quotes Smart's own words: 'I have a greater compass both of mirth and melancholy than another.'

In his Seatonian poems Smart showed true religious feelings, giving indications of the theme which he later developed in the *Jubilate Agno* and in the *Song to David*. This theme, the summoning of all nature and all mankind to unite in praise of the Creator, did not drive him to exhibitions of extreme piety until illness hastened the unbalancing of a mind already impaired by poor living and by drink. According to his own statement prefacing the *Hymn to the Supreme Being, On Recovering from a*

37

Dangerous Fit of Illness, he was seriously ill three times before 1756.

Smart's mind was not seriously affected when he wrote this poem, though it indicates the morbidly religious trend which made him contrast his illness with that of Saul and which, during his derangement, found expression in the *Jubilate Agno*, and when he was recovering, in the *Song to David*.

His madness seems to have manifested itself exclusively in violent praying. Dr. Johnson's famous friend Hester Lynch Piozzi said that 'In every *other* transaction of life no man's wits could be more regular'. As the desire to pray increased, his addresses to God were made at more and more irregular and more and more frequent intervals. All sense of time and place deserted him, and he would call his friends from their dinners, beds, and entertainments, to come out into the street and join in his devotions. 'For I blessed God in St. James's Park till I routed all the company', he wrote, adding, 'For the officers of the peace are at variance with me, and the watchman smites me with his staff.' It is recorded that Dr. Johnson in 1762 visited the mad poet in his cell and prayed with him: 'I'd as lief pray with Kit Smart as any one else.'

Noyes has pointed out that with Section VII of the *Jubilate Agno*, written in the middle of 1759, there is marked change of tone, due to Smart's anger at action taken or projected against him. 'For I am not without authority in my jeopardy, which I derive inevitably from the glory of the name of the Lord. . . .' Assuming this to be true, it seems likely that the lines 'For I meditate the peace of Europe amongst family bickerings and domestic jars. . . . For I bless God in the rising generation, which is on my side . . .' refer to Smart's two children looking on while their mother and grandparents discussed their best course of action. In a later passage there is evidence that he was persuaded to make some assignment before

entering into what might prove to be permanent confinement: 'For I this day made over my inheritance to my
mother in consideration of her poverty. For I bless the
thirteenth of August, in which I had the grace to obey
the voice of Christ in my conscience.'

From then onward there is no continuity of thought
until this line occurs to suggest that he had once more
been committed to an asylum: 'For they have separated
me and my bosom, whereas the right comes by setting us
together.' Then there are lines which doubtless refer to the
custom of allowing visitors to gaze upon the inmates of
the eighteenth-century asylum and even to torment them:

'For Silly fellow! Silly fellow! is against me, and belongeth neither
to me nor my family . . .
For they pass by me in their tour, and the good Samaritan is not
yet come.'

Yet Smart's life in the asylum, whether it was Bethlehem,
St. Luke's, or a private establishment, was far from
unhappy. He was allowed writing materials, newspapers,
and the company of his cat, Jeoffry. 'He digs in the
garden', Johnson told Burney, and in the *Jubilate Agno*
the poet wrote, 'The Lord succeed my pink borders'.

There is only one reference to ill-treatment, soon after
the supposed date of his confinement: 'For they work me
with their harping-irons, which is a barbarous instrument,
because I am more unguarded than others.'

The *Jubilate* affords a unique opportunity to study the
workings of a mind affected by monomania. Though it
contains passages that are completely unintelligible, the
poem is remarkable for its wealth of knowledge in the
fields of literature, both classical and contemporary,
science, and philosophy.

Most touching, perhaps, are those passages in which the
poet remembers his family: 'God be gracious to my wife',
and 'God be merciful to my wife', and one in which the

tragedy of Kit Smart is brought starkly before us as he thinks of his children: 'For I pray God to give them the food which I cannot earn for them any otherwise than by prayer.' In strange contrast to the voluptuous poetry of his youth he now wrote, 'For *Chastity* is the key of knowledge as in Edras, Sir Isaac Newton and now, God be praised, in me'.

In his piety he prayed, not only for all mankind, but for all the animal world: 'God be merciful to all dumb creatures in respect of pain,' he wrote, and his ability to see spiritual significance in all things is exemplified in such lines as: 'For he purrs in thankfulness, when God tells him he's a good cat,' and 'Let Ehud rejoice with Onocrotalas, whose braying is for the glory of God, because he makes the best music in his power.'

In the closing pages he shows how much he resented being confined: 'I am under the same accusation with my Saviour—for they said, he is beside himself.' It is interesting to remember that even in his college days his persecution complex had been strong, and in the *Jubilate* he constantly reverts to the theme in such lines as 'God considere thou me for the baseness of those I have served very highly'. For one with an unfortunate reputation for drunkenness, whom Dr. Johnson had described as walking to the alehouse and being carried back, he had a remarkable conviction of his own innocence: 'For I have abstained from the blood of the grape, and that even at the Lord's table,' he wrote.

These later pages also provide conclusive proof that he was planning a version of the psalms of David. 'The Lord magnify the idea of Smart singing hymns on this day in the eyes of the whole University of Cambridge. Novr. 5th 1762. N.S.'

The exact date of Smart's release is not known. The *Song to David* was published on April 8, 1763, and in a letter dated July 30 Boswell wrote to Sir David Dalrymple:

'Poor man, he has been relieved from his confinement, but not from his unhappy disorder. However, he has it not in any great height.'

Smart, now aged forty, was once more engaged in poetry and translations. His financial status was made more secure when a friend obtained for him a Treasury pension of £50 a year. In October, 1769, he called on the Burneys, and as Fanny tells us in her diary: 'Poor Mr. Smart presented me this morning with a rose, blooming and sweet as if we were in the month of June. "It was given me", said he, "by a fair lady—though not so fair as you. . . ." ' This piece of flattery made little impression upon the sensible young woman, who remarks that such utterances might be taken as evidence of his infirmities. This was probably his last act of gallantry, for shortly afterwards he was taken to King's Bench Prison, where his brother-in-law, Thomas Carnan, secured him the rules of the King's Bench, which meant that he enjoyed the freedom of a restricted area during the hours of daylight. His friends once more rallied round him and raised a subscription to augment his small prison allowance.

In 1770 he issued *Hymns for the Amusement of Children*, his last literary production. Simple and charming, these poems showed that the goodness and sweetness of his character could survive the most cruel blows of fate. It was not long, however, before his sanity again gave way, when he sought to forget his afflictions by drinking. Once again his habits brought him to extreme want, and he wrote to a friend: 'Being upon the recovery from a fit of illness, and *having nothing to eat*, I beg you to lend me *two or three shillings*, which (God willing) I will return, with many thanks, in two or three days.'

At last hunger and drunkenness brought about the inevitable conclusion to the tragedy, and Kit Smart, barely forty-nine years of age, died in the rules of the King's Bench. His death was ascribed to disease of the liver, which, as Noyes says, one might guess to have been cirrhosis.

The Flea that Became an Eagle

One day Dr. Johnson, asked whether Samuel Derrick or Christopher Smart was the better poet, made this crushing reply: 'Sir, there is no settling the point of precedency between a louse and a flea,' and it was this remark that provided the sub-title for Dr. Russell Brain's article. With the exception of the lines *On An Eagle Confined in a College Court*, Smart's writings in the lucid days before madness overtook him contain little to cause any one to dispute Johnson's judgement. That great Cham of literature acted as a true friend to his brother-writer when he was in need, but he made no attempt to 'whitewash' him.

In the *Jubilate Agno* and the *Song to David* the Flea did, in truth, become an Eagle. The *Song to David* was written when he had almost recovered and when, as Dr. Russell Brain says, he experienced moods of extreme elation. The momentum of sinking excitement gave him not only heightened emotional tension, but a feeling for words which enabled him to write as he had never written before. This sensation of excitement and elation is known to produce in sufferers from mania 'flights of fancy' which liberate latent creative power. In Dr. Brain's view Smart's mental illness was not the result of drunkenness, but he drank immoderately because he was mentally unstable.

The *Jubilate Agno* contains the lines, 'For in my nature I quested for beauty, but God, God hath sent me to the sea for pearls'. Though much of his life was passed in squalor and privation, that quest was successful because he had the gift to see beauty in all living things. It is amusing to reflect that when his collected poems were issued in 1791, twenty years after his death, the *Song to David* was omitted as affording a 'melancholy proof' of mental derangement. In contrast, Robert Browning likened the *Song* to an exquisitely beautiful chapel set amid a huge house where all else is drab:

> 'Song, where flute-breath silvers trumpet clang,
> And stations you for once on either hand
> With Milton and with Keats.'

Physically Smart was undersized, and in one of his odes he apologized for being a little man. Judging from his portraits, his eyes were grey, though according to the *Cambridge Chronicle* he was a 'little, smart, black-eyed man'. In manner he was abnormally nervous and retiring, but could be most amiable once this shyness was overcome. In the company of children he was full of drollery and high spirits. Shortly before he entered the King's Bench Prison, Fanny Burney described him as 'extremely grave', with 'still great wildness in his manner, looks, and voice'. According to the diarist he lived out his last days 'under the alternate pressure of partial aberration of intellect, and bacchanalian forgetfulness of misfortune'.

The Thorn in the Nightingales' Breast

> 'Never nightingale so singeth:
> Oh, she leans on thorny tree
> And her poet-song she flingeth
> Over pain to victory.'

So wrote Elizabeth Barrett Browning in *The Lost Bower*. Reflecting on the many great poets who in hours of madness have given to the world their most enduring works, one may well wonder whether true poetry requires the stimulus of some mental derangement for its release from the soul. There is certainly food for thought in the story of Christopher Smart, whose greatest poem, *Song to David*, was written with a key on the walls of his madhouse cell. What went on in the mind of this extraordinary man when he wrote his strange blend of haunting beauty, sensuous imagery, and engrossing incoherence, we cannot even guess. Let us be satisfied with Laurence Binyon's intriguing suggestion that when Smart composed this poem, madness did not destroy his intellect or understanding but merely affected an estrangement of his mind from his century.

> 'Great wits are sure to madness near alli'd,
> And thin partitions do their bounds divide.'

WALT WHITMAN (1819–92)

The Invert who Sought to Redeem Democracy

> 'To be conscious of my body, so satis-
> fied, so large!
> To be this incredible God I am.
> I am an acme of things accomplished.'

THOUGH recognition came to this strangest and most
explosive figure in American literature during his lifetime, he was not at once accepted as the national poet of
his country. His early works were almost wholly concerned
with Whitman, as typifying the great human personality;
in later poems the idealism remained, the laudation of
national democracy persisted, but the presentation was
more objective. Many deny that Whitman was a poet at
all. His endless, irregularly accented, unrhymed lines were
not calculated to make a universal appeal. The peculiar
prose which the author and his disciples falsely baptized
verse and a later generation designated *vers libre*, was
written in a form deliberately chosen by this son of a Long
Island farmer, for he considered traditional verse-form
a hindrance to free expression. After experimenting for
some time, he succeeded in freeing himself from the
shackles of convention, producing an effect which is as
uncouth as it is striking. The finest of his poems have a
strangely beautiful cadence, majestic as the voice of the
ocean, elemental as the raging storm. Inevitably his
ebullient work aroused in many of his contemporaries profound admiration and hyperbolic eulogy; in others it produced disgust and loathing. Listen to Swinburne's vicious
comments: 'He is a writer of something occasionally like
English, and a man of something occasionally like genius.
. . . A drunken apple woman reeling in a gutter,' and his
muse he described as 'a Hottentot wench under the
influence of cantharides and adulterated rum'.

45

Walt Whitman was born in Huntington on Long Island, on May 31, 1819. He had English, Welsh, and Dutch blood in his veins. His father, a man of strongly radical tendencies, was a small farmer who later became a builder. As a boy Walt was 'a big, good-natured lad, clumsy and slovenly in appearance, but not otherwise remarkable'. In 1824 the family moved to Brooklyn, where the boy amplified the knowledge acquired by voracious reading, in studying the varied types of people in the city. When taken on trips to Long Island he was able to satisfy his passion for bathing and to indulge in the contemplation of his own body: 'I loved, after bathing, to race up and down the hard sand, and declaim Homer or Shakespeare to the surf and sea-gulls by the hour.'

At the age of eleven he was employed as office-boy by a lawyer, whose son gave him a subscription to a circulating library—a present which enabled him to read the works of Scott and the *Arabian Nights*. He soon left the lawyer's office to work for a doctor, but in his thirteenth year changed jobs once again, this time becoming a printer's devil on the *Long Island Patriot*. Whitman filled many posts in various parts of the country, and in the period 1836–41 he taught in seven schools and acted as editor of the *Long Islander* at Huntington. His verses written during 1838–9 were conventional. Described as 'a dreamy, impracticable youth', he was even then 'inordinately indolent' and 'morose'. Whether teaching or typesetting, his thoughts seemed more occupied with the books which came his way. The Bible, Shakespeare, Ossian, Homer, Scott, Dante, the Nibelungenlied, and the Hindu poets were then his companions.

A Hidden Romance

He took an active part in the Polk-for-President campaign of 1844, and at one time frequented Tammany Hall, but for the most part he preferred to brush shoulders with the city crowds. Associated with at least ten different newspapers between 1841 and 1848, he began to write for the *Democratic Review*, which brought him into contact with some of the foremost figures in American literature. In 1846 he edited the Brooklyn *Eagle*, but was dismissed from this post in January, 1848, because he had protested against the failure of the Democratic party to face the issue of slavery. In that year he was already experimenting in sexual themes. While working for the *Eagle* he had reviewed Goethe's Autobiography, a book which made a great impression on him, for in Goethe he saw a man who had explored the universe in terms of himself. A love affair with an octoroon in New Orleans is said to have had a profound influence on his character. On the subject of this hidden romance in his life Edgar Lee Masters, in *Whitman* (1937) quotes an article by Emory Holloway in *The Dial* for November, 1920. Holloway had seen the original manuscript of 'Once I Pass'd through a Populous City' and found no mention of the woman featured in the version published in the 1860–1 edition of *Leaves of Grass*. In the original manuscript Whitman wrote: 'But now of all that city I remember only the man who wandered with me there for love of me.' His statements, however, are often notoriously unreliable. In 1890, for instance, he wrote to John Addington Symonds: 'My life, young manhood, my mid age, times South etc., have been jolly bodily, and doubtless open to criticism. Though unmarried I have had six children. . . .' There exists no evidence to support this statement. One woman, at least, fell completely under his spell. Mrs. Anne Gilchrist, widow of a London art critic and mother of four children, who had read William Michael Rossetti's abridged edition of *Leaves of Grass*, was completely swept off her feet and wrote to tell Whitman: 'It was the divine soul embracing mine. I never before dreamt what love meant.' Her letter remained unanswered, as did later extravagant effusions. In May, 1870, she published an 'Estimate of Walt Whitman' in the *Boston Radical*, and having heard from the poet continued to write rapturous epistles. In January, 1876, Whitman learned that the lady had taken tickets for a transatlantic crossing. He managed to dissuade her, but he later made the mistake of falling ill, whereupon Mrs. Gilchrist with three of her children promptly went to Philadelphia. After almost daily entertaining her idol to tea, she began to realize that he was not the marrying kind and returned to England, where she died at the age of 85. Dutifully Whitman composed a poem to her memory.

Leaves of Grass

The reception accorded the first edition of *Leaves of Grass* (1855)—a slim volume of twelve poems printed at the author's expense—was chilling. No more than a dozen copies were sold, and some of the presentation copies were returned with insulting comments. Copies of this same first edition have fetched staggering sums in recent years. Whitman wrote an anonymous review of the work, describing himself as 'of pure American breed, large and lusty . . . a naive, masculine, affectionate, contemplative, sensual, imperious person', and carried his deceptions even further. The second edition of 1856, which bore the unauthorized inscription, 'I greet you at the beginning of a great career, R. W. Emerson', included new poems of lust, as 'A Woman Waits for Me':

'It is I, you women, I make my way,
I am stern, acrid, large undissuadable, but I love you,
I do not hurt you any more than is necessary for you,
I pour the stuff to start sons and daughters for these States,
I press with slow rude muscles,
I brace myself effectually, I listen to no entreaties,
I dare not withdraw till I deposit what has so long accumulated within me.'

In this volume the thoughtfulness and beauty of the 'Song of the Open Road' and 'By Blue Ontario's Shore' are intermingled with such lusting monstrosities as these lines from 'Spontaneous Me':

48

WALT WHITMAN
(1819–92)

'Love thoughts, love-juice, love-odour, love-yielding, love-climbers,
 and the climbing sap,
Arms and hands of love, lips of love, phallic thumb of love, breasts
 of love, bellies press'd and glued together with love.'

Whitman's experiences in the Civil War affected his
health. Serving as a volunteer amateur nurse, he spent
long hours in the wards carrying gifts for the wounded,
writing their letters, dressing their gangrenous wounds,
and assisting at operations. He appears to have contracted
malaria during this period, and also developed blood
poisoning. The constant suffering he witnessed made a
deep impression on his sensitive mind and enriched the
sincerity of his pen. In June, 1864, he wrote to his mother:
'Mother, I have not felt well at all the last week. I had
spells of deathly faintness and bad trouble in my head
too, and sore throat. . . .' Three days later he wrote that
the doctor had told him he had continued too long in the
hospitals, absorbing too much of the 'virus' in his system.
In July, 1863, he received a cut on his right hand while
assisting in the amputation of a gangrenous limb. The
hand became inflamed and swollen, and red streaks ran
up to the shoulder. In those days erysipelas was a dreaded
scourge, running from bed to bed and believed to be
following the direction of the wind as it blew through the
room.

In January, 1865, Whitman was appointed to a clerk-
ship in the Indian Bureau of the Department of the
Interior, but was dismissed in the following June because
exception was taken to certain immoral passages in *Leaves
of Grass*. He succeeded, however, in securing a post in the
Attorney-General's office, an engagement which termin-
ated on June 30, 1874, some fifteen or sixteen months after
he had been stricken with paralysis. When the poet was
being attacked at the time of his dismissal from the
Department of the Interior, his disciple John Burroughs
published a defence in *Notes on Walt Whitman as Poet
and Person*. It was not until after Burrough's death that

it was learned that Whitman had written most of the work!

While employed in the Attorney-General's office, the poet formed a friendship with Peter Doyle, a Washington street-car driver. Many of the letters which he wrote to this young man were published by Dr. R. M. Bucke in a book entitled *Calamus—A Series of Letters Written during the Years* 1869–1880 *by Walt Whitman to a Young Friend*. These epistles were couched in affectionate language: 'Dear boy and comrade', 'Take care of yourself, Dear Pete, we will soon be together again', 'my darling boy', 'Dear Pete, dear son . . . Good night, my darling son—here is a kiss for you, dear boy . . .', 'I pass my time alone, and yet not lonesome at all (often think of you, Pete, and put my arm around you and hug you up close, and give you a good bus—Often)'.

The editor of these letters mentioned that he had in his possession others written by Whitman to various young men, and pointed out that the section of the *Leaves* which he called 'Calamus' proved that he had experienced friendships 'equally warm and tender'. Horace Traubel, who for many years played Boswell to Whitman, was a small boy when he first met the poet. He has recorded that at the time people warned his mother against allowing the boy to associate with 'the lecherous old man'.

The Invalid

On the morning of January 24, 1873, Whitman woke to find that he was paralysed down his left side. He had enjoyed good health until 1858, when he complained of suffering from 'sunstroke'—probably the first of a series of minor strokes. When he was tending the wounded during the Civil War he thought the men were cheered by his healthy appearance: 'I am so large and well—indeed like a great wild buffalo, with much hair.' His development had been rapid. He described himself as a

'Healthy, strong youth (grew too fast, though, was nearly as big as a man at 15 or 16)'. Burroughs said Whitman was in 'no sense a muscular man, an athlete. His body, though superb, was curiously the body of a child. One saw this in its form, in its pink color, and in the delicate texture of the skin.'

The hand injured in July, 1863, was 'thoroughly healed' in August, but in the summer of that year he complained that the sun affected him, causing 'aching and fulness on the head'. This trouble continued; he suffered 'spells of deathly faintness', and a severe attack in 1869 left him with little use of his limbs. Throughout the 1870's and 80's he was troubled by sick spells. In 1885 he was seen by Doctor (later Sir William) Osler, a superb clinician who has recorded some remarkable impressions of his patient. When Osler, who was then living in Philadelphia, received a telegram from Dr. Bucke, the words 'Please see Walt and let me know how he is', conveyed nothing to him, and he was obliged to reply, 'Who is Walt and where does he live?' When enlightened on this point Osler remembered that some time previously he had heard Bucke praise Whitman in terms so extravagant that he had doubts of his sanity, for the psychiatrist 'classed him with our Saviour, Buddha, and Mahomet'.

Osler found the poet almost recovered from a recent attack, with only slight residual weakness in his left leg as a reminder of the paralysis of 1873. After making his examination he told Whitman that 'the machine was in fairly good condition considering the length of time it had been on the road'. The poet's appearance at this time is vividly described by his physician: 'With a large frame, and well-shaped, well poised head, covered with a profusion of snow-white hair, which mingled on the cheeks with a heavy long beard and moustache, Walt Whitman in his sixty-fifth year was a fine figure of a man who had aged beautifully, or more properly speaking, majestically. The eyebrows were thick and shaggy, and the man seemed lost in a hirsute canopy.'

51

Of the Kindred of High Priest

At the time of this visit Osler had never read a line of Whitman's poetry, and in his club library that evening he took his first glimpse into the pages of *Leaves of Grass*, but was promptly disillusioned: 'Whether the meat was too strong, or whether it was the style of the cooking—'twas not for my pampered palate, accustomed to Plato and Shakespeare and Shelley and Keats.' In recording this impression Osler mentioned that even the worshipping Bucke had told him that on his first reading of it he saw 'absolutely nothing in the book'. On one occasion Osler invited Bucke and a few friends to dine and steered the conversation round to Whitman. 'Though a hero-worshipper, it was a new experience in my life to hear an elderly man—looking a venerable seer—with absolute abandonment tell how *Leaves of Grass* had meant for him spiritual enlightenment, a new power in life, new joys in a new existence on a plane higher than he had ever hoped to reach. All this with the accompanying physical exaltation expressed by dilated pupils and intensity of utterance that were embarrassing to uninitiated friends. This incident illustrates the type of influence exercised by Whitman on his disciples—a cult of a type such as no other literary man of our generation has been the object.' It may here be recalled that Bucke urged people in England to travel to America for the sole purpose of gazing at the poet's ear, 'the most magnificent ear ever modelled and fixed on the head of a man'.

By shocking the puritans, by his blatant self-advertising, and by violating every law of versification, Whitman constantly exposed himself to attack. His poems of nakedness have been ascribed to the survival of a youthful exhibitionism, but seem more likely to have been inspired by recollection of boyhood days in the country and on the beaches. Despite his declaration that he had fathered six illegitimate children there is no evidence that he ever had any affairs with women. His attitude to sex is contradictory, for he desired, but apparently had nothing to do with women. In his notes on the meaning and intention of *Leaves of Grass* he wrote:

'All through writings preserve the equilibrium of the truth that the material world, and all its laws, are as grand and superb as the spiritual world and all its laws. Most writers have disclaimed the physical world and they have not over-estimated the other, or soul, but have under-estimated the corporeal. How shall my eye separate the beauty of the blossoming buckwheat field from the stalks and heads of tangible matter? How shall I know what life is except as I see it in the flesh? I will not praise one without the other or any more than the other.'

In 'I Sing the Body Electric' he says 'The love of the body of man or woman balks account', and in his curious liking for cataloguing mentions every part of the human anatomy from head to foot 'man-balls, man-root . . . The womb, the teats, nipples, breast-milk, tears, laughter, weeping, love-books, love-perturbations and risings. . . .' The poem ends:

'The curious sympathy one feels when feeling with the hand the naked meat of the body,
The circling rivers of the breath, and breathing it in and out,
The beauty of the waist, and thence of the hips, and thence downward toward the knees,
The thin red jellies within you or within me, the bones and the marrow in the bones,
The exquisite realisation of health;
O I say these are not the parts and poems of the body only, but of the soul,
O I say now these are the soul!'

Whitman was fifty-four years old when he suffered a paralytic stroke in 1873. After making a partial recovery he

started out for the Jersey coast, but broke down in Philadelphia and was taken to his brother's house in Camden.
At the end of 1881 he bought the house, 328 Mickle
Street, where he spent the remainder of his life. For the
greater part of the years which were left to him he was
confined to the house, but he made short visits to the West,
to Canada, Boston, and New York. He occupied himself
with seeing successive editions of the *Leaves of Grass*
through the Press, and, surrounded by an astonishing
litter of books, newspaper-clippings, proofs, and manu-
scripts, he received his many visitors.

Writing on Christmas Day, 1888, he recorded: 'Am
somewhat easier and freer today and the last three days—
sit up most of the time—read and write, and receive my
visitors. Have now been indoors sick for seven months—
half of the time bad, bad, vertigo, indigestion, bladder,
gastric, head trouble inertia. . . .' The exceptionally hot
summer of 1891 tried him severely, and in December of
the following year he had a chill which developed into
pneumonia. Though the doctors thought he could live
no more than a day or two, he lingered until March 26,
1893, when, between the hours of six and seven in the
evening he died peacefully. With life slowly slipping
away, he had cheerfully awaited the end: 'Death is like
being invited out to a good dinner.'

At a postmortem examination the old man was found
to be a veritable museum of pathological conditions. The
right lung was practically useless, only one-eighth being
suitable for breathing purposes. The cause of death was
given as pleurisy of the left side, consumption of the right
lung, general miliary tuberculosis, and parenchymatous
nephritis. In addition the poet had a fatty liver, gall-
stones, and tuberculous abscesses eroding bones. His
premature senility and the paralysis which dated from
1873 gave rise to much speculation. Many of his enemies
attributed these to abnormal sexuality and gross indulgence, but the poet did not lack defenders. John Burroughs
wrote: 'I have known Whitman for nearly thirty years, and
a cleaner, saner, more wholesome man in word and deed,

I have never known. If my life depended upon it, I could not convict him of one unclean word, or one immoral act.'

The Enigma

In many ways, Whitman the man and poet to this day remains an enigma. He sang of the common man, but the common man never understood him. The prophet and loudspeaker of a cosmic democracy, he was rejected by the people whom he loved, panegyrized, and dignified with his pen. He tried to look on sex matters with sanity, but his interest in such matters was attributed to the basest motives. Surveying the great American nation he saw a great opportunity for poetry. He loved life, his fellow-man and womankind; he loved democracy. The communion and fellowship which he extolled has undoubtedly been one of the greatest influences in American literature.

Whitman never smoked, and drank very moderately. Scrupulously clean in his person, he liked to bathe his hands and face with eau-de-Cologne. He was extremely sensitive, and easily excited by things and persons that touched him. He has been called auto-erotic, erethistic, homosexual. Some people, rather loosely, speak of a higher, a sublimated, form of homosexuality. It is a difficult question, for there is much that is obscure in Whitman's life. He can scarcely have been sexually normal, but if he loved man more than woman, he claimed that this gave him clearer insight into the principles upon which democracies could hold together.

So tremendous was the impact of this remarkable man on remarkable people that he succeeded in raising adoring disciples to the stature of high priests who spoke with the tongue of hyperbole and wrote with the pen of spiritual intoxication: William Michael Rossetti, Havelock Ellis, John Addington Symonds. And it was Symonds who wrote this almost unbelievable encomium:

55

'He is the circumambient air, in which float shadowy shapes, rise mirage towers and palmgroves. He is the globe itself; all seas, lands, forests, climates, storms, snows, sunshines, rains of universal earth. . . . He comes to us as lover, consoler, physician, nurse; most tender, fatherly. . . .'

ALGERNON CHARLES SWINBURNE (1837–1909)

Epilepsy and Genius

> 'I will go back to the great sweet mother,—
> Mother and lover of men, the Sea.
> I will go down to her, I and none other,
> Close with her, kiss her, and mix her with
>   me;
> Cling to her, strive with her, hold her fast;
> O fair white mother, in days long past
> Born without sister, born without brother,
> Set free my soul as thy soul is free.'
>
> *The Triumph of Time.*

MOP-HAIRED, carroty; a head so big that his was the largest topper at Eton; white face, receding chin; all resting upon narrow, sloping shoulders and a puny body. Twittering, jerking wrists; the whole set in motion on excitable, twinkling feet. This extraordinary figure was Algernon Charles Swinburne in his younger days.

He was born on April 5, 1837, in Chester Street, Grosvenor Place, London, and nobody expected him to survive more than an hour. But he did survive and, in the bracing air of the Isle of Wight where the family settled shortly afterwards, grew into an active and healthy, if not robust, schoolboy.

Swinburne took pride in his family tree. He may, indeed, have sometimes adorned it with illustrious though fanciful names, even referring when in a loquacious mood to his descent from the Marquis de Sade or to 'some fusions of Hotspur's lineal blood in direct descent'. But certainly, from the time of Edward II the Swinburnes had figured among the gentry of Northumberland, and since Elizabeth's day they had been established at Capheaton. His father was Admiral Charles Henry Swinburne, red-headed too, bluff and kindly, but with a healthy distrust of literature and the arts. The son resembled much more, and found a more kindred spirit in, his mother, Lady Jane

57

Henrietta, daughter of the third Earl of Ashburnham. Educated abroad, chiefly in Florence, and a woman of wide culture, she would sit for hours reading to her children from French and Italian literature. Perhaps it was in the nursery, from the intonations of her lovely voice, that Algernon first caught the melody of word-sound.

Swinburne's childhood, spent 'between the sea-cliff and the sea', in Bonchurch on the Isle of Wight, was serene and happy. For companions he had his Gordon cousins living four miles away, and a healthy rivalry grew up between the two families. Summer holidays were spent at Capheaton in Northumberland, at the ancestral home, then in the possession of the grandfather—a firm favourite of the young Swinburne.

The Great Sweet Mother

It was during these Bonchurch days that the boy grew to love the sea—the one point which he held in common with his father. The sea is a recurrent theme of his best poetry and an unending source of poetic images and symbols. In it he found both emotions in harmony with his own, and emotions defying his own—now unbroken calm; now wild stimulation; physical strength he might at times match—for he was a fine swimmer, yet one that was ever too mighty to conquer. It was, in fact, his constant physical, spiritual, sensual, emotional inspiration. Yet, strangely, when he attempts to describe it pictorially, the inspiration is gone from him. The storm he encountered once when crossing the channel at the age of eighteen seems to have provided one of his deepest experiences, for he refers to it times without number in his poems. He remembers being afraid of many things, but never of the sea. Besides being an experienced swimmer, he was also in his youth an adventurous horseman and daring climber. Though he avoided the more conventional forms of exercise, battling with the elements seems to have afforded him immense satisfaction: the sting of the surf against naked body; the scratch and bruise of bare rock; the whistling of the wind against white cheeks and through auburn mane. Hurt, self-given, turned to joy. He had learnt that there is a sensual component in suffering pain.

His love for the breaking sea was a complex passion. The resounding ocean was the voice of freedom and liberty of soul at a time when the echoes of the French Revolution with the breaking of idols and the crumbling of ideals had scarcely died away.

In 1849 Swinburne went to Eton where, apart from good work in French and Italian, his career was as undistinguished in the classroom as it was on the playing fields. He did, however, read widely, extending what was already a deep, but circumscribed knowledge of literature; exploring Dickens, Shakespeare, and the Elizabethan and Jacobean dramatists. He seems to have been happy enough in his school days, on which in old age he could look back with affection and write:

'Still the reaches of the river, still the light on field and hill,
   Still the memories held aloft as lamps for hope's young fire to fill.'

For some reason or other he appears to have got into trouble and left Eton at the age of sixteen.

So his childhood seems to have been ordinary enough and typical of a Victorian youngster of his social standing. Apart from his striking appearance and his intolerance of criticism there was nothing out of the ordinary about him, nothing to hint at the eccentric behaviour of later years; nothing, apart from a few odd scraps which he is reputed to have torn up before going to Oxford, to show in which direction his genius lay.

At Oxford, in the home of the Regius Professor of Medicine, Sir Henry Acland, whom he frivolously called the 'Rose of Sharon', he found life uncongenial. He does not seem to have been an over-popular figure there; in fact, he was a little shunned. At first he reverted temporarily to the High Church persuasion of his family, for the influence of the personalities of the Oxford Movement were still to be felt down the corridors of Balliol. But in his second year he came under the spell of John Nichol, republican and free-thinker, who formulated in Swinburne's mind his hitherto vague republican tendencies. Swinburne spoke in the Union in heated defence of Mazzini and Orsini, the would-be killer of Napoleon III, and adorned his room with portraits of both. The posthumously published *Ode to Mazzini* dates from this time.

And it was John Nichol who first introduced him to drink.

While at Oxford he met also the little band of Pre-Raphaelites who were engaged one long vacation, and well into the Michaelmas term too, in redecorating the walls of the Union debating-room. A speedy intimacy was established with Burne-Jones and Morris; the friendship with Rossetti was of slower development but of more permanent significance.

Under the more stabilizing and sagacious influence of Benjamin Jowett, Swinburne obtained a second class in Moderations and the Taylorian Scholarship in French and Italian. It was a bitter disappointment that his entries for the *Newdigate* were twice rejected.

The Songster Gives Voice

Meanwhile, the songster in him was beginning to give voice. The *Ode to Mazzini* was scarcely successful, but 1858 saw the completion of the more mature *Rosamund* and *Queen Yseult*.

The intemperate habits encouraged by John Nichol led Swinburne into many excesses. Jowett advised a year away from Oxford, but on his return he soon fell again into his old ways and finally left the University in 1860 without obtaining a degree. 'My Oxonian career culminated in total and scandalous failure.' His feelings for Oxford remained bitter to the end; when at the age of 71 he was offered an honorary degree, he gracelessly refused.

Perhaps the various intellectual enthusiasms of Swinburne's early years have been over-stressed, particularly as his fame rests on his power of song rather than of thought, but they have a special significance. It is interesting in this connection to note Harold Nicolson's comment that 'Swinburne's emotional receptivity began to ossify in 1857, that is in his twenty-first year. The experiences which he had by then absorbed became his future attitudes. . . . The sea, the sun and wind had been absorbed in childhood; with Eton came Sophocles, Sappho, the *Birds* of Aristophanes, Catullus, the Elizabethans, Landor, Hugo, Mary Queen of Scots; during his first year at Balliol there flamed for him Mazzini and the detestation of Napoleon III. This strange assortment remained throughout his life the essential stimulus: there is no stimulus after 1857 that became really essential.'

A New Hero

In 1861 a copy of the writings of the Marquis de Sade fell into his hands. He had found a new hero. It cannot be said simply that these aroused sadistic tendencies in Swinburne; they rather confirmed and fed tendencies which, incipient but harmless in childhood, were already present in his undergraduate days and manifested in the early *Rosamund* and *Queen Yseult*.

Admiral Swinburne's displeasure at the sudden and scandalous conclusion to his son's career at Oxford can be imagined, but after a tactful absence in Northumberland, and aided by his mother's intervention, the son was restored to favour and was granted a generous annual allowance of £400.

So he came to London, took rooms in 16 Grafton Street, Fitzroy Square; renewed Pre-Raphaelite acquaintances; finally moved into Rossetti's Tudor house in Cheyne Walk, Chelsea. In 1862, among other London adventures, he fell in love with a charming and vivacious young lady who, though she encouraged him with roses, and played

61

and sang to him, laughed in his face when he proposed to her. Smarting, Swinburne retired again to Northumberland. As he recovered his emotional equilibrium, he wrote the lovely *Triumph of Time*. The following spring he went to Paris and there became acquainted with Whistler. Meanwhile, his alcoholic excesses continued, unchecked.

Alcoholic Epilepsy

It was in early 1863 that the poet had the first of the epileptic, or epileptiform, fits which, precipitated by excitement or emotion, were to be a continuous embarrassment and anxiety to his friends. It has been said that he never suffered from genuine epilepsy. Epilepsy usually begins in childhood or adolescence, whereas Swinburne was twenty-six when he had his first seizure. Besides, no mention is made at any time of the suffused face and frothing lips which characterize the epileptic during a fit. And there does not seem to have been any hereditary tendency to epilepsy in either his father's or his mother's family. It seems more probable that Swinburne suffered from the type of the disease known as alcoholic epilepsy, for since his undergraduate days he had been rapidly acquiring the habit of hard drinking, consuming quantities of brandy far beyond his constitutional and nervous capacity. Alcoholic epilepsy results from chronic alcoholic toxaemia or poisoning, and when the attacks begin after adolescence, they are barely distinguishable from true epilepsy.

Sir Edmund Gosse, a sympathetic biographer, was startled one day on entering the British Museum Reading Room to see that 'Swinburne had fallen in a fit while working . . . and had cut his forehead superficially against the iron staple of the desk. I was walking along a corridor', he relates, 'when I was passed by a couple of silent attendants rapidly carrying along in a chair what seemed to be a dead man. I recognized him instantly from his photographs which now filled the shop windows. His hanging hands, closed eyelides, corpse-white face, and red hair dabbled in blood presented an appearance of the utmost horror, but I learned a few days later that his recovery was rapid and complete.'

Once Swinburne had a fit in Whistler's studio; another time he collapsed at Lord Houghton's breakfast table. Many a time the Admiral was summoned urgently to find his son in what appeared to be final collapse. Although after a fit the victim is often dazed and may complain for a while of headache, the poet's recovery was invariably rapid, and, if anything, he seemed all the better afterwards, both physically and mentally. It was, in fact, while he was recuperating on the Isle of Wight after the fit in Whistler's studio that *Atalanta in Calydon* was completed. What a novel and startling experience it was for the author to find that this book was actually beginning to pay!

While it would be unwise to draw too close a parallel between Swinburne's epilepsy and certain qualities in his poetry, this intriguing aspect of his work has not received overmuch attention. In the healthy brain, nerve energy, under the control of the will, can be expended in a sudden, even explosive, but carefully regulated manner. In epilepsy it is a sudden, uncontrolled, purposeless discharge of energy that takes place. This is manifested in temporary unconsciousness or disorientation, and in convulsive movements. Aggressiveness and destructive tendencies come often to characterize the epileptic, particularly the alcoholic epileptic. It is precisely these qualities, the explosiveness, the at times ill-organized use of the poetic inspiration in his mind, and the note of aggressiveness which can so often be detected in Swinburne's work.

It is worth while reading through the lovely *Hesperia* with these points in mind. Besides its unsurpassed effects of word melody and its metrical variety, it has a wide emotional range, though not emotional depth; within less than a hundred lines, emotional tension is built up in a remarkable manner—in this respect it might be worth the attention of choreographer or orchestrator.

In the first line, to heighten by contrast what is to

follow, slow-paced, drawn-out vowels and lengthening
spirants shed serenity:

> 'Out of the golden remote wild west where the sea without shore is,
> Full of the sunset, and sad, if at all, with the fullness of joy,
> As a wind sets in with the autumn that blows from the region of
> stories,
> Blows with a perfume of songs and of memories beloved from a
> boy, . . .'

Already, albeit imperceptibly, the pace moves on 'with
the pulse of invisible feet', till an abrupt change of
emphasis and rhythm sharpens the emotional tone. 'Pity,
. . .' he spits out the word—'explosive'.

> 'Pity, not love, that is born of the breath and decays with the blood,
> As the cross that a wild nun clasps till the edge of it bruises her
> bosom,
> So love wounds as we grasp it, and blackens and burns as a flame.'

Then the aggressive note in the half line:

> 'I have loved overmuch . . .'

Meanwhile brief monosyllables, explosives and short
vowels help to quicken the pace:

> 'I have loved overmuch in my life; when the live bud bursts with the
> blossom,
> Bitter as ashes or tears is the fruit, and the wine thereof shame.
> As a heart that its anguish divides is the green bud cloven asunder;
> As the blood of a man self-slain is the flush of the leaves that allure;
> And the perfume as poison and wine to the brain, a delight and a
> wonder;
> And the thorns are too sharp for a boy, too slight for a man to
> endure.'

Fleeting, unfinished images jostle with each other; tension
is heightened by every poetic device of sound and association; words of emotional and sensuous content combine
with intricacies of metre—but without structure or out-
lines—'ill-organized':

64

ALGERNON CHARLES SWINBURNE
1837–1909

'By the thundering reef and the low sea-wall and the channel of years,
Our wild steeds press on the night, strain hard through pleasure and
    peril,
Labour and listen and pant not or pause for the peril that nears;
And the sound of them trampling the way cleaves night as an arrow
    asunder,
And slow by the sand-hill and swift by the down with its glimpses
    of grass,
Sudden and steady the music, as eight hoofs trample and thunder,
Rings in the ear of the low blind wind of the night as we pass.'

So onwards, to the finale, the breaking point, the explosion:

'Shrill shrieks in our faces the blind bland air that was mute as a
    maiden,
Stung into storm by the speed of our passage, and deaf where we
    past;
And our spirits too burn as we bound, thine holy but mine heavy-
    laden,
As we burn with the fire of our flight; ah love! shall we win at the
    last?'

Success and Failure

Swinburne's success in drawing-rooms and in intellectual circles was immediate and overwhelming. A new singing voice was sweetly and passionately heard, strangely disquieting the adolescent heart with haunting melodies and dreams of loneliness, of fervour, of unutterable loveliness. Ushered in by his friends in the now fashionable Pre-Raphaelite circle, his *Atalanta in Calydon* was acclaimed by the intelligentsia, in a state of *ennui* and waiting for a surprise, as something new and unexampled in English poetry. Success was his, and he liked it. But, unfortunately, it brought out some of his less admirable characteristics. At dinner-parties he would get drunk and aggressive; personal relationships grew strained; friendships waxed cold.

Poems and Ballads, published in 1866, enjoyed a *succès de scandale* throughout Victorian England. *Punch* devoted an editorial to Mr. 'Swineborn', and one reviewer spoke of the author as 'an unclean fiery imp from the pit', as 'the libidinous laureate of a pack of satyrs'.

Again notoriety went to his head. Arrogant and intractable, his anti-social behaviour alienated good friends and attracted less reputable ones. In 1867 Adah Isaacs Menken, a stalwart, five-times married American schoolteacher and actress, who was then appearing in the sensational spectacle *Mazeppa* in Astley's Circus, became his mistress.

The poet's literary output continued to be phenomenal. Yet, as his popularity among the reading public at large increased, so the enthusiasm of his own circle of friends waned. Possibly they were disappointed by the obvious lack of purpose and development in his life and work. And in personal habits, too, he seemed to be growing more and more aloof from human existence. He grew impervious to external influences; the early 'ossifying' process left him in a state of immaturity; impulses and energies were thus diverted, perverted. Thus his work falls short of the greatest of the great; it fails to achieve the universal, for its source is in not merely the particular, but in the eccentric. It was his personal tragedy that remote and distant, even at the moment of success, perhaps nonetheless he realized he was losing touch with letters, art, politics, with life. The red mane dulled to a sandy colour; the shoulders drooped just a little; the sprightly feet were a shade slower. He might be seen any day eating alone in some restaurant, or walking along a busy London street, courteous, even distinguished, but abstracted. His days were filled with increasing monotony and loneliness. Deep depression alternated with moods of violent arrogance, even moods of persecution mania. His aggressiveness which he had never learned to subdue, would still burst out; watch how he suddenly loses his temper when writing about Keats:

'The *Ode to a Nightingale*, one of the finest masterpieces of human work in all time and for all ages, is immediately preceded in all editions now current by some of the most vulgar and fulsome doggerel ever whimpered by a vapid and effeminate rhymester in the sickly stage of whelphood.'

He consoled himself with solitary bouts with the brandy bottle.

In January, 1878, John Nichol and he spent one last uproarious, saturnalian month together in Glasgow. The strain, of course, was too much; by May, Swinburne was too ill to accept Victor Hugo's invitation to be present at the Voltaire centenary celebrations in Paris. By the winter he was an old man, gladly accepting a hand to help his tottering feet up a flight of stairs. The following year he moved to new rooms in Guilford Street, Russell Square, but he took the brandy bottle with him, and in September he contracted acute alcoholic dysentery and seemed on the point of a squalid death.

Sometime in the early 1870's Swinburne had placed his affairs in the capable hands of the St. Ives lawyer, Walter Theodore Watts, later Watts-Dunton, who at the age of forty stepped smartly into literary circles of London. Out of the purely business association, a friendship grew up between the two bachelors: soon they were spending holidays together on the Suffolk or Yorkshire coast, and Swinburne came to rely on Watts-Dunton to keep him in touch with everyday life.

From what seemed like being a death-bed in Bloomsbury lodgings Swinburne was now transferred by Watts-Dunton to his semi-detached suburban villa at the foot of Putney Hill. Bohemian days were over; slowly the poet was nursed back to comparative health, and life was well-ordered for the thirty years more that he was to live—a morning walk over the Common; an afternoon's rest; in the evening work in his study. Regular, unruffled days, except for the little flutter of excitement in 1882, when the two men were invited to Paris by Victor Hugo for the jubilee performance of *Le Roi s'Amuse*. But, pathetically, Swinburne's deafness prevented his hearing a word Hugo was saying to him over the private dinner they had together. Under the Watts-Dunton régime Swinburne's literary output continued to be enormous, but too obviously the mark of Watts-Dunton, both in form and content, is set upon his work; the fire has gone out of it.

In 1903 he caught pneumonia. Remarkably, he recovered, but both lungs were affected. The daily routine was taken up again for a while, though a little more slowly, but the fires were burning low. In 1909 Watts-Dunton fell ill with influenza. Swinburne insisted on visiting the sick-room, with *Ivanhoe* clasped in his frail hands, ready to read to the patient. The following day, regardless of wind and rain, he took his usual stroll over Putney Common, to return a tired old man. Two days later he had pneumonia with both lungs affected. He became delirious, but suffered little pain. He died gently on April 10, 1909, at the age of 72. He is buried in the rocky cemetery of his fathers at Bonchurch, not far from the water's edge, where he knows for ever 'the slow passionate pulse of the sea'. When he died, the light died for the world, and in the sudden darkness the young grew suddenly old. The song of spring, so ethereal, so short-lived, was heard no more in the land, and yet, even to-day, in a much more prosaic and essentially unlovely world, we can open our Swinburne and can recapture for a few fleeting moments that lust for the sweetness of life which was **ours** when we and the world were young.

EDGAR ALLAN POE (1809–49)

The Oedipus Complex and Genius

'He knelt with Virtue, kissed with Sin—
Wild Passion's child, and Sorrow's twin,
A meteor that had lost its way!'

EDGAR ALLAN POE was born in Boston, Massachusetts, in 1809, the second son of David and Elizabeth Poe, both minor luminaries of the contemporary American stage. The parents were poor, being without private means and dependent on their stage earnings, and this probably meant that the members of the family had to be satisfied with their own immediate small circle, friendships and social contacts with the inevitable expense of entertaining being beyond their means.

From his earliest days Edgar Allan Poe was abnormally attached to and dependent on his mother. This early propensity, unavoidable in the circumstances, towards an Oedipus complex was intensified both by the character and behaviour of an alcoholic and consumptive father of dubious faithfulness to his wife. In any case he disappeared from the scene when Edgar Allan was scarcely more than a year old, and the child's circle grew even narrower, with a consequent intensification of his attachment to his mother. She was a lovely, sylphlike woman, with the wide forehead and the large, mysterious eyes that characterized her son, and though she never made any mark on the stage, seems to have possessed considerable histrionic talent. Her lack of success in her profession was probably due in part to a life of poverty and financial worries and also to ill health. She suffered from tuberculosis and died in extreme penury at the end of 1811, when her son was in his third year. This small child, with his still younger sister, no doubt witnessed the slow death of the woman upon whom alone they had depended for every care and affection. The whole circumstances of his mother's short unhappy life and untimely death affected him profoundly, and his emotional fixation to her memory is evident throughout his works. His feelings for her were manifested in two states of mind: firstly the protective attitude —almost maternal, if one may term it so, that subsequently characterized many of his affairs with women, the most notable example being his platonic attachment to his child wife, Virginia Clemm; secondly, the usual Oedipus complex epitomizing his relationship with his mother in his youthful regard for Mrs. Jane Stanard, whose memory inspired one of his most famous poems 'To Helen'.

> 'Helen, thy beauty is to me
> Like those Nicean barks of yore,
> That gently, o'er a perfumed sea,
> The weary, wayworn wanderer bore
> To his own native shore.
>
> On desperate seas long wont to roam,
> Thy hyacinth hair, thy classic face,
> Thy Naiad airs have brought me home
> To the glory that was Greece
> And the grandeur that was Rome.'

It is epitomized, too, in his love for Maria Clemm, the woman who after his break with John Allan in the eighteen thirties gave him as much care and affection as if he had been her own son.

The Mother Complex

Poe's psychic life was dominated by this Mother Complex and his preoccupation with her death, as he writes:

> 'I could not love except where Death
> Was mingling his with Beauty's breath.'

In 1842 his young wife Virginia had her first lung haemorrhage and thus approximating more closely to Poe's erotic ideal, intensified his unconscious longing for his dead mother: *Ligeia* and *The Fall of the House of Usher* being symbolical illustrations of his feelings on this theme.

Like so many other victims of this particular psychological disturbance, Poe suffered from sexual abnormality, in which the unusual love for the mother unconsciously breeds a dislike, and often an abnegation, of the normal sexual impulse. This facet of his character is evident in his tale *The Murders in the Rue Morgue*, in which, according to an analysis by Marie Bonaparte, the orang-outang is symbolic of the brutal male, the murder represents the sexual attack on the mother, and the sailor witnessing the assault is the young Edgar Allan. A natural corollary of this abnormal sexual attitude was the impotence of psychic origin that afflicted the poet and was derived originally from his unconscious fixation to his dead mother and later reinforced by his addiction to opium.

After his mother's death Poe was separated from his sister and adopted by John Allan, a Scotsman who had emigrated to America. He was a dour unsympathetic individual, and though he seems to have taken a pride in the precocious pretty ways of the child, treated him with scant sympathy and a good deal of stern discipline, and probably only consented to having him at all in response to repeated pleadings on the part of his wife. The woman was tolerably affectionate, and though most of young Poe's physical needs were met, it could hardly be called a happy household, and the natural reaction of the boy was to withdraw even more into his shell. As a result he became neurotic, his mother fixation was emphasized, and he remained maladjusted to the problems of reality. Life, he probably felt, had given him a raw deal.

Refuge in Alcohol

This was the situation when in 1826 Poe entered the University of Virginia and, once free of the parental discipline, took refuge in alcohol, to the effects of which he was unfortunately more susceptible than most men. His was that distressing form of alcoholism in which it is not so much the drink itself that has an attraction, but the sense of well-being and subsequent oblivion which indulgence brings in its train. The taste and smell of alcohol remained abhorrent to him all his life. When engaged in literary pursuits, he certainly did not resort to a stronger mental stimulant than coffee, and that but sparingly.

His University career was short and unsuccessful socially, though academically he distinguished himself both in Latin and French, and was in excellent standing with the authorities. His foster-father kept him woefully short of money, and Poe's attempt to remedy this deficiency by card playing landed him hopelessly in debt, whereupon Allan withdrew his 'son' from the University in great indignation.

During this period Poe became engaged to Sarah Elmira Royster, but her parents disapproved, and his association with her was broken off. Subsequently she married someone else but was left a widow and in 1849 had promised to marry Poe, but he died before they could realize their dream.

After his departure from the University, Poe and his father disagreed about his career: Allan wishing him to take up law and Poe being intent on literary pursuits. As a result he left home and entered West Point where he was surprisingly successful and rose to the rank of Regimental Sergeant Major. Although he was only twenty-one, he looked so weary and worn that it was jokingly whispered the appointment had really been obtained for the son who had meanwhile died, when the father came to fill the vacancy. All[1] this time he was wretchedly short of money and, though in 1839 when his foster-mother died, he and Allan were temporarily reconciled, it was an uneasy relationship. Poe, however, did his best not to alienate his father unnecessarily, being hopeful of inheriting ultimately a portion of the legacy that had fallen to Allan from an uncle. But once more life cheated him: Allan remarried, and Poe quarrelled with the second wife and was ordered from the house. To add to his misfortunes he neglected his studies and was dismissed from West Point in 1831. For the rest of his life he made a precarious living by various forms of literary work, but he never achieved financial security and experienced periods of distressing poverty. Tragic though this was, in view of the fortune that his works were destined to earn after his death, it was partly his own fault, and his failure can be attributed to his peculiar neurotic and introspective mind. For instance, he ruined his chances of obtaining a Government post and possible support for a literary journal on which he had set his heart, by indulging in a heavy drinking bout just before an advertised lecture in Washington and an interview with the President in the White House.

After Poe's dismissal from West Point he went to live with his father's sister, Maria Clemm, and his relationship to her was more intense than the normal mother–son attitude and was probably an outward manifestation of his unremitting concentration on the memory of his own mother. Soon he began to attract considerable notice and in October, 1833, won a prize of $50, with *A MS found in a Bottle* for the best short story submitted to the *Baltimore Saturday Visitor*. In addition to the monetary award the young author gained the friendship of John P. Kennedy, who became his patron and introduced him to T. W. White, editor of the *Southern Literary Messenger*. Poe now began to contribute to this paper, his literary and poetic genius enlivening its pages. But again his temperament failed him, he resorted to excessive drinking to ward off melancholia, and his connection with the paper was temporarily broken.

Aged 27, Poe now decided to marry his cousin, Virginia Clemm, a child of 13, consumptive, frail, exquisitely beautiful. His love for her was never of the flesh, being of a platonic non-physical nature, and his resentment against life intensified as he watched her slowly breaking up before the onslaught of that same insidious disease that had robbed him of his mother. In fact, in marrying her he was most certainly trying to restore the situation in which he had found himself as an infant, with Virginia epitomizing

73

the mother relationship. This explains the brother–sister standing of the wedded couple, which took the place of that of the normal husband and wife.

Virginia's story is one of the most poignant in the annals of literature, and her husband's tenderness for her constitutes one of the noblest and most endearing incidents in an essentially unlovely and at times sordid life. Virginia died in January, 1847, on a mattress of straw, covered by the poet's overcoat, with a yellow tortoise-shell cat curled up on her bosom for extra warmth. So wretchedly poor was Poe at the time that he could not afford to buy blankets for his dying wife. All his earthly days she continued to live in his mind, and her shadow broods over the pages of his writings to this day, for she was the prototype of many of his heroines: 'and then all is mystery and terror, and a tale which should not be told. Disease, a fatal disease, fell like the simoon upon her frame; and even while I gazed upon her, the spirit of change swept over her, pervading her mind, her habits, and her character, . . . disturbing even the identity of her person.'

The psychological trends of Poe's character, the main one being the Oedipus complex, made him incapable of combining the spiritual and physical aspects of love and caused him to be impotent with women for whom he had any regard. His indulgence in opium and alcohol can be attributed to these psychological peculiarities: opium allowed him to indulge in dreams of his beloved mother and satisfied him spiritually, whereas alcohol took the place of the physical side—by its kindly oblivion the poet kept himself faithful to the memory of his mother and avoided physical intimacy with living women.

Escapist Drugs

Poe's indulgence in these two 'escapist' drugs—opium and alcohol—was one of the methods by which he fought the intolerable morbidity of his manic-depressive state of

mind and sought a temporary forgetfulness of the misfortunes and setbacks to which he seemed predestined.
Had this been his only weapon to relieve the depressions
that overtook him, he would, like thousands of others
similarly afflicted, have lived his life unknown and gone
unsung by posterity. But he had a second weapon—his
pen. Thus he provides a typical example of the classical
Greek theory, so convincingly put forward by Aristotle in
his *Poetics*, of the cleansing of the soul's excessive emotions
by an intensive concentration on the states of mind that
produce them. To watch a Greek tragedy purified the soul
by ridding it of its excessive feelings of pity and fear. In
exactly the same way, by committing his sado-necrophilic
and morbid psychological urges to paper Poe achieved a
catharsis of these overriding emotions and a temporary
respite from his grief. An obvious example of this can be
found in *The Black Cat*, where the hanging of the cat
symbolizes the hanging of Jocasta in the Oedipus drama,
and Poe's concentration on this theme temporarily relieved
his soul of its burden of sorrow and yearning for his long
dead mother. Had he not been possessed of his peculiar
mother-complex much of his more macabre writing, by
which he is perhaps best known, would never have been
produced.

Shortly after his marriage to Virginia Clemm he was
reinstated as editor of the *Southern Literary Messenger* and
this time had more success until over-indulgence in
alcohol, probably resulting from worry about Virginia's
health, made his tenure of office once more precarious.
Dissatisfied in any case with his progress on this paper he
left for New York in 1837, but after a short interval of
penurious living in that city came back to Philadelphia
where he tried his hand at independent publishing, worked
as editor of *Burton's Gentleman's Magazine* for about a
year, and then attempted to start a magazine of his own,
The Penn Magazine. Plans for this, however, were
abandoned in favour of an offer to become editor of the
newly established *Graham's Lady's and Gentleman's Magazine*. In this Poe achieved moderate success, but alcohol

once more proved his undoing, and the rest of his stay in Philadelphia was marked by abject poverty, with Virginia's health rapidly failing and Poe seeking an escape from his miseries in frequent drinking bouts. It was at this time that he began to write mystery and horror stories, notable among which were *The Murders in the Rue Morgue, The Mystery of Marie Roget*, and *The Gold Bug*.

To New York he went again in 1844 where he achieved temporary success with the *Broadway Journal*, but again failed to curb his propensities for alcohol, and 1846 saw the last number of the magazine.

Poe's health was now deteriorating, and his heart gave him increasing trouble. He attempted to satisfy his longing for sympathy and understanding by seeking the company of women, and his adventures in this field during his last years are more fantastic if anything than were those of his early days. Conspicuous among his *inamorata* of this time was Mrs. Mary Shew, who was his inspiration for *The Bells* in 1848, and Mrs. Annie Richmond for whom he seems to have cherished an exalted form of passion which encouraged him to attempt once more to launch his own magazine—the ill-starred *Stylus;* but again he found himself lacking in the mental stamina to resist the craving for alcohol, and the project was in consequence a failure. A certain Mrs. Whitman was the next object of his affections, but the counter-charms of Mrs. Richmond could not be lightly forgotten, and Poe, in a moment of intense despair and uncertainty, tried to commit suicide by taking laudanum. 'When the day broke, I arose and endeavored to quiet my mind by a rapid walk in the cold, keen air—but the Demon tormented me still. . . . Finally I procured two ounces of laudanum.' Mrs. Whitman eventually promised to marry him on condition that he gave up alcohol, but again he lacked the necessary control and following another lapse, she finally refused to go through with the marriage.

In all these attempts to find a sympathetic woman to share his life now that Virginia had died, Poe was even then, when approaching forty years of age, seeking to satisfy his unconscious longing for his mother and to rid his soul of the grief which had obsessed him since her death in his earliest, most impressionable days. His last year was a strange period of vacillation between excessive lapses into drinking bouts and complete abstention. He even went so far as to join a lodge of teetotalers and for a short time fought down his desire for alcohol. But in the autumn of 1849, when planning to marry one of his old loves—Sarah Elmira Royster—he fell for the last time a victim to his besetting weakness, whether by his own fault or as a result of falling foul of a gang of 'repeaters' during a few days of intense political pre-election fever. He was found in a semiconscious state at a low tavern on the water front of Baltimore, and taken to the Washington University Hospital where he died four days later of delirium tremens after a short unhappy life of some forty years.

Poe's life thus ended at an age when most men have barely reached their prime or the zenith of their powers, but he had accomplished enough in that short time to perpetuate his memory not only in the English-speaking world, but—thanks to the subsequent translations of his works by Baudelaire—on the continent of Europe.

The Man and the Poet

Edgar Allan Poe was about five feet eight inches in height, straight and slender, with raven black curly hair, chalky complexion, and melancholy features. His eyes were dark grey, luminous, and magnetic, and under the influence of excitement became vivid and penetrating. His mouth was small and weak, and his teeth were perfect. His hands were shaped like the claws of a bird. The haunting beauty of his face was heightened by the scars of life's defeat. Essentially a man of sorrow, he smiled but rarely, and no one had ever heard him laugh aloud. How perfectly the description of Roderick Usher in the *House of Usher* fits the poet himself! 'A cadaverousness of

77

complexion, an eye large, liquid, and luminous beyond comparison, lips somewhat thin and very pallid, but of a surprisingly beautiful curve, a nose of a delicate Hebrew model, but with a breadth of nostril unusual in similar formations; a finely moulded chin, speaking in its want of prominence, of a want of moral energy; hair of a more than weblike softness and tenuity; these features with an inordinate expansion above the regions of the temple, made up altogether a countenance not easily forgotten.'

Poe's voice was exquisitely modulated, and from his parents he had inherited a natural ability as orator and actor.

As a man Poe was a miserable failure. He could not get on with his fellows, and his relationships with women were fantastic to read about and undoubtedly disastrous to experience. But it was precisely the characteristics which made him a failure socially that ensured his success in the literary world. His genius was exceptional and was the result of his peculiar temperament—it was a fire that his unhappy psychological make-up served not to quench, but to fan into pure and lasting brilliance.

CHARLES LAMB (1775–1834)

The Genius who Resented the Impertinence of Manhood

'Dream not, Coleridge, of having tasted
all the grandeur and wildness of fancy
till you have gone mad.'

'I RUN no great risk in asserting that, of all English
authors, Charles Lamb is the one loved most warmly
and emotionally by his readers.' These words of that
kindly critic, Augustine Birrell, are sufficientre commenda-
tion to make those unfamiliar with the works of Charles
Lamb desirous of meeting the sweetest spirit in the history
of English literature. Others owe their introduction to,
and their eager pursuit of Lamb to one of the least
pedantic of teachers, innocent alike of profoundness and
of superficiality. Biographer, critic, and editor of Lamb,
E. V. Lucas with his inimitably light touch and his
Lambian fondness for trifles, succeeded so delightfully
in making them catch the echo of his hero's stammering
urbanity, adore his simplicity, his infinite variety, his
exquisite understanding, his quips and conceits and
obliquities.

Scholars and critics have lavished their time, their
learning, and their eloquence on the intriguing task of
canonizing 'St. Charles', yet few writers have given us so
many intimate glimpses of the man as may be found in his
incomparable *Essays of Elia*. How casually and how
vividly the author peeps at us from its pages with his
sweet smile and his hauntingly sad eyes!

In this year of grace 1951 what could possibly be said
that is new about one who externally belonged but little
to his time and generation? 'Damn the age! I will write
for antiquity.' From a purely biographical approach one
shrinks as it were instinctively. Have we not all become
infected with Lamb's own adorable failings? In *Witches*

79

and Night Fears and in *Dream Children* we read of his childish fears and superstitions, while a tribute to 'the late Elia' provides us with a remarkably penetrating analysis of his own character:

> 'His manners lagged behind his years. He was too much of the boy-man. The *toga virilis* never sate gracefully on his shoulders. The impressions of infancy had burnt into him, and he resented the impertinence of manhood.'

The Stock from Which I Spring

Charles Lamb was born in Crown Office Row, Inner Temple, London, on February 10, 1775. 'I was born and passed the first seven years of my life in the Temple. Its church, its halls, its fountains, its river—these are my oldest recollections.' His father, John Lamb, was clerk and confidential servant to Samuel Salt, a Bencher, and is portrayed by Charles as Lovel in the essay *The Old Benchers of the Inner Temple*. From a passage in *New Year's Eve* it appears that the boy had smallpox when he was five years of age, and in *Dream Children* he mentions being carried 'many a mile' upon the back of his brother John 'when he was lame-footed'. A weakly child, he learned to speak with difficulty, stammering all his life.

After attending a day school near Fetter Lane, at the age of seven he was admitted to Christ's Hospital, where he remained until 1789. His memories and impressions of schoolfellows and masters are embodied in two famous essays. Samuel Taylor Coleridge, who was two years his senior, became his close friend, the two developing a tender, lifelong regard for each other.

On leaving school Lamb took a post in the South Sea House, an appointment which he owed to the good offices of Samuel Salt. Although he remained there for a short period only, leaving to become a clerk in the accountant's office of the East India House, the South Sea House and those who worked there were enshrined in yet another memorable essay. His life from then onward might have followed the humdrum round of any London clerk of those days, but though he remained in his job for thirty years, there was certainly no ordinary pattern in his life. Into that period fall many of the essays which were to establish his reputation as the most finished essayist of all times. In that period, too, he came face to face with stark tragedy—tragedy which put him to a test as severe as ever man experienced. During this time of heartbreak and dire necessity he managed to live heroically, keeping faith with life and with himself.

In 1796 Charles, his parents, and his sister Mary took lodgings at 7, Little Queen Street, Holborn, for with the death of Samuel Salt the family had vacated their quarters in The Temple. Poverty was then their lot, for Charles's salary and the small amount which Mary earned by her needlework had to suffice for four people. The father, whom premature senility had sought out in his fiftieth year, was slowly failing in health and was to die insane. The mother was capricious and hysterical, and when her son was twenty-one years old, she became a bed-ridden paralytic. She is said to have been a victim of moral anaesthesia.

It was on September 22, 1796, that Charles was called upon to shoulder the burden which he relinquished only at his death. Mary Lamb was a morbidly shy girl, yearning for affection which her mother was so incapable of giving her. The task of nursing an invalid mother and of trying to amuse a peevish, unbalanced father proved too great a strain. Charles himself was not quite free from the family taint of insanity. Disappointment in love at the critical time of puberty precipitated a mental breakdown which necessitated his temporary restraint. In a letter to Coleridge he wrote later:

'The six weeks that finished last year and began this, your very humble servant spent very agreeably in a madhouse at Hoxton. I am somewhat rational now and don't bite anyone. But mad I was . . . Coleridge, it may convince you of my regards for you when I tell you my head ran on you in my madness, as much almost as on another Person: who I am inclined to think was the more immediate cause of my temporary frenzy.'

We have the authority of Southey for the statement that during this troubled period Lamb believed himself to be young Norval in Home's *Douglas*. A sonnet to Mary written in one of his lucid intervals at Hoxton ran as follows:

'If from my lips some angry accents fell
Peevish complaint or harsh reproof unkind,
'Twas but the error of a sickly mind.
And troubled thoughts, clouding the purer well
And waters clear of reason.'

At times Lamb was to look back upon this interlude, not in any fearful apprehension of a relapse, but 'with a gloomy kind of envy, for while it lasted, I had many, many hours of pure happiness. Dream not, Coleridge, of having tasted all the grandeur and wildness of fancy till you have gone mad.'

On the evening of September 21, 1796, Mary Lamb showed signs of mania, and on the following morning her brother called at the address of Dr. Pitcairn but failed to find him at home. Later that day Mary, in a fit of violent rage, stabbed her mother to the heart with a table knife, killing her instantly. Charles came into the room to find his aunt apparently dying, his father with a wound on his forehead, and his mother murdered. On the 27th he wrote to tell Coleridge of the tragedy:

'. . . My poor dearest sister in a fit of insanity has been the death of her own mother. I was at hand only time enough to snatch the knife out of her grasp. She is at present in a mad house . . . thank God I am very calm and composed, and able to do the best that remains to do. . . .'

His 'best' meant the care of his aged, demented father and of his aunt Hetty, who had a witchlike habit of muttering to herself. For them he had to provide a home till the end of their days. When Mary had so far recovered that permanent restraint was judged unnecessary, her brother gave the Home Secretary 'his solemn engagement that he would take her under his care for life'. Her cyclothymia (a mental condition characterized by alternating elation and depression) was to last for half a century, for she survived her brother by nearly thirteen years. Lamb sacrificed everything in caring for those he loved. Returning from the drudgery of his office desk, he was expected to play cribbage with his old father who, in the selfishness of senility, was too impatient to wait while his son had his evening meal. The following passage in a letter to Coleridge is eloquent of Lamb's forbearance:

> 'I am starving at the India House, near 7 o'clock without my dinner, and so it has been and will be almost all the week. I get home at night o'erwearied, quite faint, and then to *cards* with my father, who will not let me enjoy a meal in peace—but I must conform to my situation, and I hope I am, for the most part, not unthankful.'

How bravely, how lightly, Lamb bore his burden of sorrow, treating it almost as though it were some huge fantastic joke!

Torn from the books he had learned to love, and from the society of his friends, he consecrated himself to the care of father and sister. In the long years of vigil he never wavered. After his father's death all his devotion was lavished upon Mary, with whom he lived until his death in 1834.

The Safety Valve

Lamb's first appearance in print was in the year his mother met her tragic end. Four of his sonnets were published in Coleridge's *Poems on Various Subjects*. Two years later a volume called *Blank Verse* contained his best-known poem, 'The Old Familiar Faces':

> 'Where are they gone, the old familiar faces?
>
> I had a mother, but she died, and left me,
> Died prematurely in a day of horrors—
> All, all are gone, the old familiar faces.

I have had playmates, I have had companions,
In my days of childhood, in my joyful schooldays—
All, all are gone, the old familiar faces.

I have been laughing, I have been carousing,
Drinking late, sitting late, with my bosom cronies—
All, all are gone, the old familiar faces.

I loved a love once, fairest among women.
Closed are her doors on me, I must not see her—
All, all are gone, the old familiar faces.

I have a friend, a kinder friend has no man,
Like an ingrate, I left my friend abruptly;
Left him, to muse on the old familiar faces.

Ghost-like, I paced round the haunts of my childhood,
Earth seem'd a desert I was bound to traverse,
Seeking to find the old familiar faces.

Friend of my bosom, thou more than a brother!
Why wert not thou born in my father's dwelling?
So might we talk of the old familiar faces.

For some they have died, and some they have left me,
And some are taken from me; all are departed;
All, all are gone, the old familiar faces.'

The friend in the fifth stanza was Lloyd; he is the seventh
Coleridge. 'And some are taken from me' refers to one of
Mary Lamb's periodic returns to the asylum. Brother and
sister lived together in perfect harmony—'old bachelor
and maid, in a sort of double singleness'. They were
accustomed to taking occasional pleasure trips, when
Charles would always pack a straightjacket with the
luggage, for any excitement was apt to precipitate in Mary
an attack of mental instability. On some twenty occasions
she had to be sent away to an asylum at Hackney. In the
intervals between her attacks she was perfectly balanced,
genial, and intelligent.

Whenever Lamb, disconsolate, returned to the loneliness of his lodgings, he would turn for consolation to the

old masters of English verse and prose, seeking forgetfulness in the company of his beloved books and in the occupational therapy of penmanship. It was Sir Thomas Browne, above all, who may be described as his intellectual progenitor and who moulded his literary style, while the Bible enriched his language. His sister, however, was apparently blind to 'the beautiful obliquities of the *Religio Medici*'.

As early as 1796 Lamb had shut out any thoughts of marriage. 'It is a passion of which I retain nothing', he wrote to Coleridge. 'Thank God, the folly has left me for ever. Not even a review of my love verses renews one wayward wish in me.'

With their kindly humour, their wealth of fancy, their refreshing laconism, their unexpected quips, their whimsical incongruity, his essays were laboriously penned and fastidiously polished until in the finished state they sparkled with perfect spontaneity and apparently effortless artistry. His excursions into the pleasant world of literature provided an emotional safety valve, which intensifies the fascination of his fascinating essays.

How inimitable are his thoughts on *The Convalescent!*

'In the general stillness, and awful hush of the house, he lies in state, and feels his sovereignity. . . . To be sick is to enjoy monarchal prerogatives. Compare the silent tread, and quiet ministry, almost by the eye alone, with which he is served—with the careless demeanour, the unceremonious going in and out (slapping of doors, or leaving them open) of the very same attendants, when he is getting a little better—and you will confess, that from the bed of sickness (throne let me rather call it) to the elbow-chair of convalescence, is a fall from dignity, amounting to a deposition.'

Lamb's letters, long, sprightly, frolicsome, have well deserved the epithet 'divine'. Listen to this delicious passage:

'It is always difficult to get rid of a woman at the end of a tragedy. Men may fight and die. A woman must either take poison, which is a nasty trick, or go mad, which is not fit to be shown, or retire, which is poor, only retiring is most reputable.'

Curiously enough, Lamb's mental health was never again impaired, and despite his many worries and sorrows he seemed never to have been in danger of another breakdown. His friends were a tower of strength to him, and Coleridge's influence helped him to find comfort in religious faith.

A Little this Side of Abstemiousness

The Preface to the *Last Essays of Elia* sheds interesting light on Lamb's attitude towards drink and tobacco:

'He was temperate in his meals and diversions, but always kept a little this side of abstemiousness. Only in the use of the Indian weed he might be thought a little excessive. He took it, he would say, as a solvent of speech . . . as the friendly vapour ascended, how his prattle would curl up sometimes with it! the ligaments which tongue-tied him, were loosened. . . .'

While it is perfectly true that there were moments in the essayist's life when he sought and found solace in inordinate quantities of Hollands gin and hot water, it must be remembered that he was but the child of his environment, the citizen of a country whose gentlemen prided themselves on being 'three bottle men'. When Faith and Hope threatened to desert his hearth, alcohol restored his spirits, making him the joy and light of every congenial company. At those sad times when his sister was away Lamb may have sought refuge in alcohol but there is no suggestion of any habitual insobriety. He watched over Mary and performed his duties at the East India House in a satisfactory manner. Occasional lapses from grace are sometimes referred to in his letters:

'It is an observation of a wise man that "moderation is best in all things". I cannot agree with him "in liquor". There is a smoothness and oiliness in wine that makes it go down by a natural channel, which I am positive was made for that descending. Why does not wine choke us? could Nature have made that sloping lane, not to facilitate the down-going? She does nothing in vain. . . . Still there is something due to manners and customs, and I should apologise to you . . . for being absolutely carried home upon a man's shoulders thro' Silver Street, up Parson's Lane, by the Chapels (which might have taught me better), and then to be deposited like a dead log at Gaffar Westwood's. . . .'

On one of his periodic visits to his friend, the Rev. H. Francis Cary, who was an assistant in the Department of Printed Books in the British Museum, Lamb had once again drunk 'not wisely', for in a letter dated 1834 he wrote:

'I protest I know not in what words to invest my sense of the shameful violation of hospitality, which I was guilty of on that fatal Wednesday. Let it be blotted from the calendar. Had it been committed at a layman's house, say a merchant's or manufacturer's, a cheesemonger's or greengrocer's, or, to go higher, a barrister's, a member of Parliament's, a rich banker's, I should have felt alleviation, a drop of self-pity. But to be seen deliberately to go out of the house of a clergyman drunk! . . . And, then, from what house! Not a common glebe or vicarage (which yet had been shameful), but from a kingly repository of sciences, human and divine, with the primate of England for its guardian, arrayed in public majesty, from which the profane vulgar are bid fly. Could all those volumes have taught me nothing better!'

There is no evidence, however, of spirit or drug addiction in Lamb's singularly robust writings. His essay, *Confessions of a Drunkard*, has been quoted in support of his habituation to alcohol, but when it was reprinted in the *London Magazine* for August, 1822, it was accompanied by a note in which he said, among other things, that 'It is indeed a compound extracted out of his long observations of the effects of drinking upon all the world about him. . . .'

'St. Charles' needs no apologists, and Augustine Birrell, in his *Obiter Dicta*, deals effectively with those who would presume to fill that rôle:

'One grows sick of the expressions, "poor Charles Lamb", "gentle Charles Lamb". . . . Charles Lamb earned his own living, paid his own way, was the helper, not the helped . . . a shrewd man, capable of advice, strong in council. Poor Lamb, indeed! Poor Coleridge, robbed of his will; poor Wordsworth, devoured by his own *ego;* poor Southey, writing his tomes and deeming himself a classic; poor Carlyle, with his nine volumes of memoirs . . . call these men poor, if you feel it decent to do so, but not Lamb, who was rich in all that makes life valuable or memory sweet. But he used to get drunk. This explains all. Be untruthful, unfaithful, unkind; darken the lives of all who have to live under your shadow, rob youth of joy, take peace from age, live unsought for, die unmourned—and remaining sober you will escape the curse of men's pity, and be spoken of as a worthy person. But if ever, amidst what Burns called "social noise", you so far forget yourself as to get drunk, think not to plead a spotless life spent with those for whom you have laboured and saved; talk not of the love of friends or of help given to the needy: least of all make reference to a noble self-sacrifice passing the love of women, for all will avail you nothing. You get drunk—and the heartless and the selfish and the lewd crave the privilege of pitying you, and receiving your name with an odious smile.'

Lamb's addiction to tobacco caused him much searching of heart, and many a time he resolved to give up smoking. Writing to Coleridge in 1803 he asks:

'What do you think of smoking? I want your sober, *average noon opinion* of it. I generally am eating my dinner about the time I should determine it. Morning is a Girl, and can't smoke—she's no evidence one way or other; and Night is so evidently *bought over,* that *he* can't be a very upright judge. May be the truth is, that *one* pipe is wholesome, *two* pipes toothsome, *three* pipes noisome, *four* pipes fulsome, *five* pipes quarrelsome; and that's the *sum* on't. But that is deciding rather upon rhyme than reason.'

And again, in *Confessions of a Drunkard*, he described tobacco's hold upon him:

'I should repel my readers, from a mere incapacity of believing me, were I to tell them what tobacco has been to me, the drudging service which I have paid, the slavery which I have vowed to it. How, when I have resolved to quit it, a feeling as of ingratitude has started up; how it has put on personal claims and made the demands of a friend upon me. How the reading of it casually in a book, as where Adams takes a whiff in the chimney-corner of some inn in Joseph Andrews, or Piscator in the Complete Angler breaks his fast upon a morning pipe in that delicate room *Piscatoribus Sacrum*, has in a moment broken down the resistance of weeks. How a pipe was ever in my

CHARLES LAMB (1775–1834) WITH
HIS SISTER MARY

midnight path before me, till the vision forced me to realize it,—
how then its ascending vapours curled, its fragrance lulled, and the
thousand delicious ministerings conversant about it, employing
every faculty, extracted the sense of pain. How from illuminating it
came to darken, from a quick solace it turned to a negative relief,
thence to a restlessness and dissatisfaction, thence to a positive
misery. How, even now, when the whole secret stands confessed in
all its dreadful truth before, I feel myself linked to it beyond the
power of revocation. Bone of my bone——'

The Likeness of the Man

In appearance Lamb was small, thin, and frail, his legs
were thin as poles, his gait was shuffling, his hair black
and sleek, his nose prominent and hooked, and his eyes
were 'full of dumb eloquence'. The grey irises of his eyes
were pebbled with red—stigmata of degeneration. He
dressed invariably in black, wearing rusty silk stockings
and thick, large, unpolished shoes. He was usually gasping
for breath.

In a tribute to 'the late Elia' Lamb spoke of his enemies,
but he never made enemies. His friends were bound to
him with the strongest ties, and though he sometimes
annoyed and teased them, none wished to forsake him.
He had known love, for in 1794 he told Coleridge of his
'disappointed hope'—an allusion to his romance with the
Alice W——n of his beautiful *Dream Children*. Then he
had worshipped at a distance the young Quakeress, Hester
Savory, at whose death he wrote the touching lines to
Hester. When he was forty-four he proposed to Frances
Maria Kelly, the charming, vivacious actress with the
'divine plain face', who in turn enslaved Fox, Byron,
Sheridan, and Dickens, but he received a tender refusal
of his written offer of marriage. His little romance, as E.
V. Lucas says, 'was over, a single day seeing the whole
drama played', but he seemed thereafter to mellow in his
disappointment and to grow in spiritual stature.

He was in his sixtieth year when he slipped on a stone
and erysipelas complicated a trivial wound. When he

died on December 27, 1834, with the names of those he had loved on his lips, Providence decreed that poor Mary be in a state of temporary mental dullness so that she could not feel the cruelty of this bitter blow. Lamb's death was as gentle and peaceful as had been his life.

In conclusion, shall we attempt to look elusive, enigmatical Lamb squarely in the face? But at once his virtuous shade slips with almost malicious delight beyond our observation and analysis. Though the man continues to be even more enigmatic than the writer, it is no exaggeration to confess that his example and precept have placed mankind under an enduring debt. For he has shown us that while we may listen with impunity to the whispering of illusions and watch with credulity the phantoms of hope, always in the end the really happy man so arranges his life that he does not expect the mellowness of old age to fulfil the promise of youth. So let us say goodbye to Charles Lamb, a man who resented the impertinence of manhood, who kept a little this side of abstemiousness, but—heaven be praised!—who was 'at his ease in the old arms of humanity'.

THOMAS DE QUINCEY (1785–1859)

Opium and Genius

'Thou hast the keys of Paradise, oh just,
subtle, and mighty opium!'

Confessions of an English Opium Eater

ON a dull rainy Sunday afternoon in the year 1804 an Oxford student on a visit to London was suffering from 'rheumatic toothache', and on the advice of a friend he obtained from a chemist's shop a phial of the tincture of opium. Returning to his lodgings, he took the first dose and sold himself into lifelong bondage to a drug which was to lift him from the utterly prosaic plain of reality into a new land free of the prejudices of time and of space. This introduction to a dream world which he was later to paint so vividly in many of his writings, coloured his whole life, inspiring one of the most remarkable books in English literature and the most famous example of auto-pathography ever penned.

Before continuing our story, it is necessary to recall that at one time there was no particular opprobrium attached to the taking of opium or of its tincture, laudanum. The drug was freely sold anywhere to all who wished to buy it, for it was the fashion to use it for a host of minor indispositions which we to-day would treat with aspirin. That there were many addicts was inevitable, but no one would have thought of looking down upon them with the eye of repugnance or even of compassion.

Despite numerous statements that Thomas De Quincey first saw the light at Greenhay, his father's house in the suburbs of Manchester, he was, in fact, born on August 15, 1785, in the city itself. A few weeks old, he was taken to a 'pretty rustic dwelling' known as 'The Farm', and the larger house which his mother called Greenhay, was not occupied till 1791 or 1792. The fifth child of a well-to-do merchant, he saw little of his father, 'a plain and unpretending man', whose health demanded that he should spend most of his time in the warmer climates of Lisbon, Madeira, and the West Indies. Thomas was in his seventh year when his father, a victim of pulmonary consumption, returned home for the last time, and during the few weeks that remained to him, the boy, being the quietest of the children, was admitted to the sick-room.

The widow and her six children were left in comfortable circumstances, and Thomas and his eldest brother, William, were sent for daily lessons to a tutor, the Rev. Samuel Hall. William, a pugnacious lad whose 'genius for mischief amounted to inspiration', landed little Thomas, who had, willy-nilly, to be his lieutenant in all his adventures, in fights with local boys from the factories and in all manner of scrapes. De Quincey in his *Introduction to the World of Strife* brilliantly describes his brother's dominance of the entire household. William had accompanied his father on many of his travels abroad. Up to the time of his return Thomas had been a melancholy boy, given to introspection, and he believed that, had he been left to himself, he would have moped himself into consumption. William considered his younger brother physically and mentally contemptible—a view which accorded with Thomas's own estimate of himself. Writing at a later date he thought that his brother's 'shock tactics' had lifted him out of the despondency into which he seemed destined to sink.

In 1796 De Quincey's mother moved to Bath, and Thomas, then in his twelfth year, was entered at the local Grammar School, where he remained for two years, gaining a reputation for his Latin verses. While at the school he suffered a curious accident. One of the masters, aiming a blow with a cane at another boy, hit the unfortunate Thomas on the head. In describing the incident to his sister Mary, he was quite jocular: 'On poor Ego did it fall. Say, Muse, what could inspire the cane with such a direful purpose? But not on my shoulder, on my *pate*, it fell,—

unhappy pate, worthy of a better fate!' It appears, however, that the blow had alarming consequences, for the
boy was laid up for some weeks in his home.

Not unnaturally, his mother refused to allow him to
return to the Grammar School, sending him instead to a
private school at Winkfield in Wiltshire, and subsequently
to the Manchester Grammar School, where boys after a
period of three years were eligible for exhibitions to Brase-
nose College, Oxford. With the £40 or £50 a year thus
provided it was thought that his inheritance of £150 per
annum would be enough for his requirements at the
University.

Life at Manchester, however, was extremely dull. The
lessons were too elementary for one of his abilities, and
the school routine, which did not seem to have included
any recreation, was far from congenial and stimulating. In
vain did Thomas entreat his mother to remove him from
the school, asking how any one could be happy 'in a
situation which deprives him of *health*, of *society*, of
amusement, of *liberty*, of *congeniality*, or *pursuits*, and
which, to complete the precious picture, admits of no
variety'. Making up his mind to run away, he wrote to
Lady Carbery, a friend of his mother's, who had called
him her 'Admirable Crichton' because she found his
conversation so amusing, so instructive, and so eloquent,
asking for £5. Having no suspicion of his purpose, the lady
at once sent him double that amount.

Early one morning in July, 1802, a few weeks before his
seventeenth birthday, he left the Headmaster's house
where he was boarded, to begin his great adventure. His
first idea was to make for the Lake District, for he was at
that time completely under the spell of Wordsworth and
was hoping he might catch a glimpse of his hero. Realizing,
however, that he could not possibly present himself as a
runaway, he decided to return home, where he happened
to find his mother's brother, Colonel Penson, on whose
advice he was given an allowance of a guinea a week on
which to support himself whilst wandering where he chose.
The boy then roamed about North Wales until November,

sometimes living at the rate of half a guinea a day, and on other days having to make his bed among the ferns and bracken.

Longing for new experiences, he forfeited his allowance and threw himself into the unknown, fascinating, and adventurous life of London. Arriving on the coach from Shrewsbury one day in November, 1802, he immediately tried to obtain a loan from Jewish money-lenders. He applied at a house in Greek Street, Soho, where an attorney who acted for a Jew named Dell had his quarters. The Jew pursued the usual policy of delay in order that the would-be borrower could be submitted to the acceptance of the most exacting terms. When De Quincey had spent his last guinea the attorney allowed him to sleep in the house for an indefinite period, but in the day-time the boy had to keep out of the way, sitting in the parks or prowling the streets.

His wanderings around Oxford Street brought him into contact with all sorts and conditions of men and women, and among them, as we know from the *Confessions*, was the sixteen-year-old prostitute, whom he called Ann of Oxford Street. The moneylender, having heard of De Quincey's acquaintance with Lord Altamont, had expressed his willingness to advance a sum of money if the noble lord would be co-security with him. De Quincey, therefore, went to Eton to try and arrange this matter, but was unsuccessful, and on his return Ann, whose kindness of heart had transformed her into a ministering angel when he was ill from want and exhaustion, had disappeared. He never heard of her again, but the thought of her remained with him always.

By some chance he was discovered by friends and went to live with his mother at Chester. In the autumn of 1803 it was agreed that he should go to the University if he wished, but that he must manage on £100 a year.

At Oxford he was known as a quiet and studious fellow who did not seek society, but whose general knowledge and conversational powers attracted attention. He now began to make a planned study of English literature,

94

maintaining his early fondness for the older writers, but at the same time not neglecting the work of his contemporaries.

In the Clutches of Opium

De Quincey first took opium in 1804, and from then onwards he was never without the drug in some form or other, using both the solid cakes of the dried substance which came from Turkey, Egypt, Persia, or India, and the liquid form, laudanum. After he had obtained relief from the neuralgia which first prompted him to take opium, he continued to experiment with the drug, finding that besides its pain-relieving properties it acted as an intellectual stimulant. Pathetically he tried to cheat himself with the glittering bubble of the illusion that in opium he had hit upon the specific for the pulmonary consumption which he imagined he had inherited from his father: 'I offered at the first glance, to a medical eye, every symptom of phthisis broadly and conspicuously developed. The hectic colours on the face, the nocturnal perspirations, the growing embarrassment of the respiration, and other expressions of gathering feebleness under any attempts at taking exercise, all these symptoms were steadily accumulating between the ages of twenty-two and twenty-four.' Opium, he asserted, enabled him to keep up and promote insensible perspiration. Medical opinion inclines to the belief that the 'gnawing pains in the stomach' which troubled him from time to time were due to ulceration of the stomach, produced by poor food and privation during his nomadic existence in Wales and in London.

From 1807 onwards De Quincey frequently absented himself from the University, and, although his name remained on the registers till 1810, he apparently left some time before then. In 1807 he had his first meeting with Samuel Taylor Coleridge, when a casual reference to laudanum brought a solemn warning from the older man to have nothing to do with the drug. Touched by Coleridge's 'cheerless despondency', De Quincey arranged through a Bristol bookseller to make him an unconditional gift of £300. Two years later he settled among the small band of literary men who were then living in the Lake District, enjoying the society of Wordsworth, Coleridge, Southey, Charles Lloyd, and John Wilson ('Christopher North').

Describing his life in 1812 he alluded to his habit of taking opium: 'And I still take opium? On Saturday nights. And, perhaps, have taken it unblushingly ever since "the rainy Sunday". . . . And how do I find my health after all this opium-eating? . . . Why, pretty well, I thank you, reader. In fact, if I dared to say the real and simple truth (though, in order to satisfy the theories of some medical men, I ought to be ill), I was never better in my life than in the spring of 1812 . . . and I hope sincerely that the quantity of claret, port or "London particular Madeira", which . . . you, good reader, have taken . . . May as little disorder your health as mine was disordered by all the opium I had taken (though in quantity such that I might well have bathed and swum in it) for the eight years between 1804 and 1812.'

The Tyranny of the Human Face

Up to 1812, then, De Quincey claimed that he had suffered no ill-effects from the gradually increasing doses of the drug. In the following year he wrote: 'I was attacked by a most appalling irritation of the stomach, in all respects the same as that which had caused me so much suffering in youth, and accompanied by a revival of the old dreams. Now, then, it was . . . that I became a regular and confirmed (no longer an intermitting) opium-eater.' At last he reached the stage where he confessed to taking as much as 320 grains of solid opium, or 8,000 drops of laudanum in one day. This, however, is undoubtedly an exaggeration prompted by the very drug by which he had become enslaved. During this period he suffered greatly from depression and from blunting of his intellect. Apart from occasional visits to London he led an uneventful life. But not altogether uneventful, perhaps, when one recalls that remarkable episode with the Malay tramp who called at the cottage, was given food and drink, and on his departure was offered a piece of opium, 'enough to kill some half-dozen dragoons together with their horses'. De Quincey experienced considerable anxiety for several days after he had seen the man bolt the piece at one mouthful. This Malay figures in some of his most vivid dreams, assuming the rôle of supervisor of tortures. What is technically termed the 'tyranny of the human face' is one of the most fiendish characteristics of the delusions of persecution.

In 1816, when he was aged thirty-one, DeQuincey married an eighteen-year-old girl, Margaret Simpson, who lived with her father at 'The Nab', a cottage near his own. Just before his marriage he 'suddenly and without any considerable effort' made a drastic cut in his daily consumption of opium, taking only 40 grains or 1,000 drops. In the picture of the cottage which he has left us he describes his collection of 5,000 books, the bright fire, and an 'eternal tea-pot', for 'I usually drink tea from eight o'clock at night to four in the morning'. After depicting his wife presiding over this scene, he comes to 'a picture of the Opium-eater', with the 'little golden receptacle of the pernicious drug at his side . . . and I apprise you that no "little" receptacle would, even in 1816, answer *my* purpose, who was at a distance from the "stately Pantheon" and all druggists. . . . No: you may as well paint the real receptacle, which was not of gold, but glass . . . it *was* a decanter. Into this you may put a quart of ruby-coloured laudanum; that, and a book of German metaphysics placed by its side, will sufficiently attest my being in the neighbourhood.'

On his reduced ration of opium he found that the 'cloud of profoundest melancholy' passed away. Once again he could grapple with the works of the more difficult writers. All too soon, however, he relapsed, increasing his allowance until he was again taking 8,000 and sometimes even 12,000 drops a day. In the *Confessions* he describes the deleterious effect upon will-power which he experienced and which confirmed the observations of his fellow opium-eater, Coleridge: how he was unable to exert himself to perform the most ordinary business, procrastinating and neglecting to attend to domestic affairs, how he left letters unanswered and bills unpaid, but all the while retaining the sense of duty which told him what ought to be done. Usually a great walker, he became physically as well as mentally inactive, falling into 'deep-seated anxiety and gloomy melancholy': 'I seemed every night to descend, not metaphorically, but literally to descend, into chasms and sunless abysses, depths below depths, from which it seemed hopeless that I could ever re-ascend. . . . Space swelled, and was amplified to an extent of unutterable infinity. This, however, did not disturb me so much as the vast expansion of time; I sometimes seemed to have lived for seventy or a hundred years in one night.'

Writing on his dreams in May, 1818, he said: 'The Malay has been a fearful enemy for months. . . . I was stared at, hooted at, grinned at, chattered at, by monkeys, by parroquets, by cockatoos. I ran into pagodas: and was fixed, for centuries, at the summit, or in secret rooms; I was the idol; I was the priest; I was worshipped; I was sacrificed. I fled from the wrath of Brama through all the forests of Asia: Vishnu hated me: Seeva laid wait for me . . . I was buried, for a thousand years, in stone coffins, with mummies and sphynxes, in narrow chambers at the heart of eternal pyramids. . . . I heard gentle voices speaking to me (I hear everything when I am sleeping); and instantly I woke: it was broad noon; and the children were standing, hand in hand, at my bedside. . . .'

In 1818 he received a copy of David Ricardo's recently published *Principles of Political Economy and Taxation*, which made a deep impression on him, and he got so far as to prepare a manuscript entitled *Prolegomena to all*

Future Systems of Political Economy. Though advertisements appeared and arrangements for printing the pamphlet had been made, once again he lapsed into the opium torpor before the manuscript was completed.

Confessions

In 1821 he moved to London where, thanks to the Lambs, he found himself amidst friends. The kindly 'Elia' invited the lonely writer to dine and pass the evening with him and his sister whenever he wished, and introduced him to the proprietors of the *London Magazine*. It was for this journal that De Quincey wrote anonymously the *Confessions*. The first article of twenty pages appeared in the number for September, 1821, and the second part in the next issue, together with an editorial appreciation of the 'deep, eloquent, and masterly paper which stands first in our present number'.

The success of this exercise in self-revelation was immediate and overwhelming, and the proprietors readily accepted further contributions which they made a point of announcing as being by 'The English Opium Eater'. Though his entry into popular literature came late, De Quincey's unique subject and the manner in which he related it were a literary sensation. When he began to write the *Confessions* in the little room at the back of 4, York Street, Covent Garden, he little dreamed that besides capturing the imagination of the magazine's readers his story would enthral a far larger audience. In 1822 the work was published separately, and ever since it has continued to intrigue and haunt the imagination of man.

The enthusiastic reception of his writings little affected the author's way of life. Uncommunicative and shy, he shunned his fellow-writers and, depressed by poor health, once more began to take opium. Despite his success, the amount he earned by writing provided but a scanty sum with which to support himself and his family at Grasmere.

In February, 1825, he wrote: 'I am quite free from opium; but it has left the liver, the Achilles' heel of almost every human fabric, subject to affections which are tremendous for the weight of wretchedness attached to them. To fence with these with the one hand, and with the other to maintain the war with the wretched business of hack-author, with all its horrible degradations, is more than I am able to bear.'

By the end of the year he was once more in Westmore-land, and in February, 1827, contributed to *Blackwood's* the famous essay, *On Murder as one of the Fine Arts*. In 1837, when he was in his fifty-second year, De Quincey was left a widower—a pitifully helpless creature to shoulder the burden of looking after six young children. Fortunately, the children had powers of self-reliance so lamentably lacking in their father, and headed by the eldest girl, Margaret, were able to fend for themselves. In order to live economically and to provide a quiet place in which their father could seek relaxation, they took a cottage near Lasswade, seven miles from Edinburgh. From 1840 onwards this was De Quincey's home, though he continued to occupy lodgings and to pursue his peripatetic career as the spirit moved him.

Never at any time had his health been good. His frail body was wracked by pain, and from youth he had suffered from 'gastrodynia' or 'gastric neuralgia', with 'a low inflammatory condition of the mucous coat of the stomach, proceeding at times to ulceration'. He had lost his teeth, and writing to a friend in 1847 he said, half in fun, half in earnest, that he had not dined 'since shaking hands with him in the eighteenth century'. Soups and other fluids, with sops of bread, and occasional morsels of meat cut up fine for easy mastication, were his staple diet.

Victory over Evil

In the year 1844 he had fought out a tremendous battle with himself. He had been taking 5,000 drops of laudanum

daily when he tried to free himself from the terrible bondage. His account of the process and the efforts he was
called upon to make shows that the puny little man
possessed courage of no mean order. Having unsuccessfully attempted to reduce the dosage, he submitted himself to the agonies of total withdrawal of the drug. Unable
to walk normally, he dragged himself round a measured
circuit of forty-four yards in the garden at Lasswade until
he had done his ten miles a day. His self-torture was not
in vain, for he found the minimum of the drug which
enabled him to endure life. Though in 1848 he went
through another bad period, he had no difficulty in keeping his use of the drug within bounds. His victory over
the monster which had for so long held him in thrall
remains one of the strangest episodes in literature.

In spite of all that he had suffered, the hardships and
privations of his youth, the constant indigestion, the consumption of fantastic amounts of opium, De Quincey was
in the seventy-fifth year of his age when he succumbed
to senile weakness. In between the periods of lucidity
there were times when he lapsed into a sleepy delirium,
dreaming mostly of children. His last words were Sister!
Sister! Sister! as if he had had a vision of his sister
Elizabeth who had died almost seventy years before.

The Elusiveness of the Man

What a strange and singularly incongruous title to have
chosen for his autobiography, *Confessions*! For Thomas
De Quincey confided in no man and in no woman.
Though we appear to know the little man so intimately
with all his frailties and sorrows of the flesh and the spirit,
long dead he still eludes posterity's attempts at portraiture.
What do we really know of him? We are familiar with his
tiny fragile figure, his boyish face 'beaming with intellectual light', his hyperbolic politeness. We can capture
the cadences of his clear and silvery voice, and in our
ears lingers the music of his exquisite conversation. We

know, too, of his many queer habits—how he would set things on fire, even his own hair; how he would accumulate books and papers until in the end no chair remained on which to sit, no bed on which to sleep. Three times he succeeded in building his daughters out of their home.

De Quincey's *Autobiographical Sketches and Confessions* bear witness to the fact that he was a highly imaginative and hypersensitive child and that the faculty of dreaming so vividly was evident before he made the acquaintance of opium. How much the dreams which he describes in *Confessions* owe to literary embellishment it is impossible to say but it is certain that in the splendour of their imagery, in their ghastly hideousness, and in their utter horror they have no parallel in literature:

'I was kissed with cancerous kisses, by crocodiles, and was laid, confounded with all unutterable abortions, amongst reeds and Nilotic mud.'

CHARLES BAUDELAIRE (1821–1867)

Syphilis, Drugs, and Genius

> 'O let me lie near thee, and sleep
> Beneath the ancient Tree
> Of Knowledge, which shall shadow thee
> Beelzebub, and me!
> While Temples of strange sins upon
> Thy brows shall builded be.'
>
> BAUDELAIRE: *The Invocation.*

THIS is the tale of Charles Baudelaire's evil fate. At the age of six he knew the sorrow of losing his father. By nine he acquired a step-father. At seventeen he was expelled from school. Out of a lonely childhood he matured into an adolescence of disillusionment. Living the traditionally gay and Bohemian life of the Latin Quarter, he contracted the disease from which he was to die only some twenty-five years later. For two years he cultivated and refined *le dandyisme* till his inheritance was squandered. From then on his was a life of poverty, sickness, mental and physical suffering, shared, off and on, with a fat mulatto woman—eyes as large as saucers, feline movements, drug and liquor crazy, unfaithful to him even with his friends and the tradesmen who crossed his threshold. He, too, developed a taste for the then fashionable drugs—opium and hashish. And when his greatest work, on which he had so pathetically pinned all his hopes, *Les Fleurs du Mal*, appeared, the courts condemned it as an outrage upon morals and decency. Broken in body and spirit, unable to halt the implacable march of his disease, he died paralysed, and speechless—a lunatic poisoned by syphilis and drugs.

Not a success story, his. But these are 'only events; not what happened'. They cannot explain by what paradox it was that from so sordid a life and from so unfruitful a soil should spring forth and mature a soul of such profound spirituality and a mind of such heightened sensibility. Nothing can explain away genius, yet by examining some of the activating forces in the life of Charles Baudelaire we can see how sorrow and suffering quickened and sharpened innate qualities which otherwise might have remained barren, and perhaps understand the contradiction of strength from infirmity, of beauty out of squalor.

I have said . . . to the Worm

Charles can scarcely have remembered his father, François Baudelaire of the snowy white hair and the courtly, old-world manners, a drawing master and once tutor to the sons of a noble house broken up by the Revolution; for he was only six years of age when the old man died. An indifferent artist, François Baudelaire may well have had a genuine appreciation of art, and he certainly fostered a love of paintings in his son.

His mother, born in England in exile, was early orphaned and was brought up in France by an old friend of her father's. Unable in her dependent position to indulge her innate love of grandeur and luxury, she gladly accepted in marriage the hand of François Baudelaire though he was over thirty years her senior. When Charles was born, the love which should have gone to a man of her own years, was released and lavished on her baby. A fond and foolish mother, her jealous love influenced the boy's development and the morbidity of his nature. When she was widowed, Caroline Baudelaire cherished her son even more, and when she was out of mourning, took him, boy though he was, to many of her social engagements. It was not long before she won the heart of the dashing Captain Aupick.

Aupick had been left a penniless young orphan. He enlisted in the ranks, was promoted till he reached the rank of general, and then was appointed ambassador, and

finally senator. Upright, honourable, rigid, and uncom-
promising, he spared none, least of all himself. His
abhorrence of debts and any shady financial dealings,
together with his dislike of affectation and eccentricity,
were later to bring about a lack of sympathy between the
two men. Yet, according to his lights, Aupick was
genuinely fond of his stepson, was proud of his intelligence,
and always treated him with the utmost fairness.

And what of Charles, who for us is the centre of focus
in this family group? A precocious eight-year-old, he may
well have felt a little thrust aside and may have imagined
he was taking second place in his mother's affections.
Aupick, considering the boy to be soft and wayward, with
military discipline despatched him as a boarder to the
Collège Royal in Lyons, and later, when the family went
to Paris, to the famous *Lycée Louis le Grand*. Charles's
scholastic performance was not outstanding, but in his
letters home he already revealed a gift for language of
artistic perfection, a mature outlook on life, and a precocious knack of 'exteriorizing' his feelings and reactions,
which enabled him afterwards to look boldly upon himself, however much it might disgust him. As he grew
towards adolescence he became conscious of the loneliness
and isolation of his nature, and of the morbid 'spleen'
which was to characterize his earlier works. Towards his
teachers he adopted an exasperatingly polite insolence and
baited them mercilessly. Already he was becoming famous
for his paradoxes and for his brilliance as a conversation-
alist. The tone of his school reports indicates beyond doubt
that he was an unsatisfactory pupil and an unhealthy
influence among the boys. Just before he sat for his
baccalauréat he was expelled. It is significant that until
then his relations with his stepfather had been friendly,
and his letters show the efforts he was making to please
him.

Released from the irksome bonds of school, Baudelaire
wished for nothing better than to be allowed to beat his
wings in the delicious air of freedom. His mother urged
him to enter the diplomatic service, but this he firmly

refused to do. Secretly he dreamt of a literary life, to the utter consternation and disappointment of the Aupicks. His mother, conscious of the uncertainty of her own girlhood, could not understand why he would not use his intelligence, connections, and influence to make his way in a settled career. For Charles, too, there was disappointment that his mother, whom he so loved, sided with her husband. Aupick acted with his usual fairness and, considering the boy still too young to make so important a decision as the choice of a career, allowed him to continue his education for another two years. So Baudelaire was nominally enrolled for a course of study at the *École de Chartes.*

The Latin Quarter

This was the most romantic and colourful period of the Latin Quarter—the days before the great boulevards of Saint-Germain and Saint-Michel were driven through it to reveal its secrets, when its maze of narrow evil-smelling streets was little altered since the days of Villon. Baudelaire quickly entered into the spirit of this student band, at one moment disporting themselves boyishly with their beribboned velvet caps in their noisy *monômes*, at the next moment cultivating every extravagance and eccentricity, priding themselves on their cynicism, their heavy drinking, their prowess in love, and indulging in their latest vices—opium and hashish. It was during these days that Baudelaire contracted syphilis.

But Baudelaire was by nature far from being the Bohemian. His fastidiousness disliked the unkempt beards and the slovenly dress and habits of his literary and artistic companions, and when at the age of twenty-one he came into his father's fortune, he promptly quitted the Latin Quarter and took a suite of rooms in the famous *Hôtel Lauzun* on the *Ile Saint-Louis.* This he furnished in the most opulent and luxurious manner, expending enormous sums on costly furniture, rich carpets and curtains, priceless art treasures, daring schemes of decoration and every device that fashion or fancy might invent. The same care that he bestowed on his apartment was lavished on his personal appearance. Sometimes he was to be seen in plain black broadcloth, tight trousers fastening under shining patent leather shoes, white silk socks, a coat with long narrow tails, a fine white linen shirt with broad, turned-back cuffs, a collar open at the neck and fastened negligently with a scarlet tie. Or, in contrast, he would wear a bright blue suit with gold buttons. Many an affectation he had too, like the live lobster he would lead through the park on a pale blue cord, or the way in which he modelled his dress and behaviour on those of Beau Brummel, assuming what he imagined to be the arrogant ways of the English aristocracy. To ward off premature baldness he anointed his scalp with a green salve, promptly generating the rumour that he had dyed his hair green. How he revelled in such notoriety! Yet his behaviour was no more abnormal than that of other members of his circle, who loved to astonish and to shock. But among them Baudelaire was distinguished by his polished manners, almost an anachronism inherited from his parents, and by the brilliance of his conversation. Which of his intimates was to divine that in Baudelaire the social graces masked a shy, solitary, morbidly sensitive nature and that pathological dread of failure which was to determine his chronic inability to start on any venture?

Vénus Noire

It was during his residence at the *Hôtel Lauzun* that Baudelaire formed a liaison with the *Vénus Noire*, Jeanne Duval, a mulatto actress at the low-grade *Théâtre du Panthéon*, in the Latin Quarter. Jeanne must indeed have been intrigued by this reserved young man who sent her expensive bouquets and stood out by his distinguished bearing from the usual student clientèle. Whether

Baudelaire was merely desiring to make himself conspicuous when he entered into this liaison, or whether he felt genuinely attracted towards one who was to bring him so much unhappiness, we cannot say, yet it is a fact that in his life, though he affected a contempt for all women, it was two women—his mother and Jeanne Duval—who played the most significant rôles.

Under Jeanne's inspiration were written all Baudelaire's erotic love poems. She was quite unable to appreciate his intellect—his need for friendship with cultivated women was fulfilled by others—but then he did not ask her to be intelligent. His obsession for her was cerebral rather than sensuous. They were to cause each other much suffering, for joy and humiliation were both to be theirs, yet with a few intervals they were to remain close, even when she was sick and no longer beautiful.

The extravagant life which Baudelaire was leading could not continue for ever, and towards the end of 1843 his creditors began to wax insistent. As always when in need, Baudelaire turned like a child to his mother for help. Though she grieved to see her son in difficulty, she knew how right was her husband in insisting she was ruining his character by giving way to him so easily. How often was this selfsame situation to recur! Torn between son and husband, the mother would vacillate, then secretly send Charles a totally inadequate sum of money, as it were a token sum which was frittered away in current expenditure and benefited no one in the slightest. And how often was to be repeated Charles's hurt at his mother's apparent doubt of his need and at her lack of generosity!

On this occasion a family council decided that as many of his debts should be paid off as was compatible with leaving him a very small annual income. This meant that he was to be burdened with the outstanding debts for many years, and these grew, as debts will, forcing him to borrow yet further sums to pay off the interest on the original debt. So the inevitable vicious circle closed in on him, and from that time on he knew no peace where money was concerned. This perpetual worry and strain precipitated the nervous attacks which were to plague him for his remaining years.

To Baudelaire, inexperienced and unprepared, the sudden change to straitened circumstances came as a shock. He tried to hide his humiliation under a cloak of disdain and indifference, so as to discourage patronage and pity, and this '*noli me tangere*' became a permanent attitude. The bitter contrast between poetic aspiration and commonplace reality (the *Spleen et Idéal* of the *Fleurs du Mal*) engendered doubt, discouragement, self-mistrust, and self-disgust, and the youthful vague melancholy hardened into 'spleen'. And slowly the incredibly handsome, long, oval face with the delicate, sensitive nostrils and the hauntingly dark eyes set itself in the melancholy, hard, cynical lines, so strikingly depicted in his later portraits. One day when sitting in a café, he attempted to end it all by plunging a knife into his breast. This temporary imbalance had one good effect in that it seemed to purge him for a while of his depression and despair. The following year, 1846, was one of his most successful—financially—with sufficient regular work, mostly in the form of book reviews.

It was but a temporary stroke of good fortune. Because of his inability to keep on terms with any editor, Baudelaire had no contract with any newspaper or journal, so with no regular income, the possibility of paying off his debts receded, and the necessity for further borrowing became all the more apparent. To complete the circle, he found it physically almost impossible to start on a piece of work, and once begun, equally impossible to maintain concentration. Thus many a promising poem or piece of prose was frustrated, and he alienated many a friend who was willing to use his influence to obtain work for him. His mother, too, seemed to him to be hardening her heart against him. He began to show violent outburst of temper, followed by long periods of depression, and this, combined with his financial difficulties, made it small wonder that he and Jeanne found increasing cause for quarrelling. As a final blow, about 1849, he had a second attack of syphilis, though he thought himself cured of the disease. *Voyage à Cythère*, written in 1850, reveals deeper suffering and distress than a man of twenty-eight would usually experience or be called upon to bear.

The Poet Awakens

Yet over these years of suffering in mind and body Baudelaire matured. In his younger days he had been proud and arrogant; sensual pleasure had been his one ideal. Now in his humiliation the sorrows and hardships of others were thrust before him, and his pride was softened. He discovered in himself an insatiable curiosity concerning the lives and sufferings of the great band of his fellow *ratés*, and so the compassion of the true poet was awakened. Through his own sufferings he came to understand the sufferings of mankind. He does not, as does Victor Hugo, clamour on this account for social reform, for he knew that even in Utopia there would always be the *désherités*, the failures, those unable to make the grade in life. A more moving, tender, and deeply human vein creeps now into his poetry, as in the *Crépuscule du Soir*, displacing the eroticism and egoistic 'spleen' of earlier years. And as, through *l'indispensable douleur* and *la fertilisante douleur* egotism and pride ebb, there comes a vision of a more profound, more spiritual, and more enduring beauty than the selfish pleasure of the senses.

The middle 1850's were years of renewed distress. Baudelaire was writing shy, anonymous love letters and poems to the *Vénus Blanche*, Madame Sabatière, the famous nineteenth-century beauty, whose Sunday evening gatherings he used to frequent. Intrigued by his undemanding devotion, she, who had never really loved before, fell madly for him, and thinking to make things easier for him, made known to him her feelings. On the instant Baudelaire's passion cooled. He desired nothing more than to be permitted to speak to her of his devotion, that she would graciously accept his worship. He wanted her a queen on a throne, a goddess. In becoming his equal, a woman of flesh and blood, she killed his illusion. His attitude to her contrasts strikingly with his attitude towards the *Vénus Noire*. The disillusionment, the indignity of his position, the remorse for causing her so much suffering, and the knowledge that salon gossip would betray his spiritual privacy, played cruelly with one so morbidly sensitive as he. *À celle qui est trop gaie* and *Hymne* were inspired by the *Vénus Blanche*.

In the same year the long awaited *Fleurs du Mal*, the only collection of Baudelaire's poems, was published, and on August 20, 1857, the author was summoned to appear before the court in the *Palais de Justice* on two charges. He was acquitted of offence against religious morality, but found guilty of offence against public morality. Six of the poems were banned, and the edition was withdrawn from circulation. So all Baudelaire's hopes were shipwrecked, and he who had only intended to write of the tragic struggle of mankind, using his own personal experience, was now stigmatized as a pornographic poet.

By the end of the year he felt a disillusioned, middle-aged man. Depression and lethargy settled heavily on him, and relations with his mother since the death earlier that year of General Aupick became even more strained. Henceforth only black pessimism, disgust with the world, and doubt of ultimate success were his.

Les Paradis Artificiels

In *Les Paradis Artificiels*—a work consisting of an article on *Haschich*, linked with a commentary (which he called *Opium*) on, and an adaptation of, De Quincey's *Confessions of an Opium Eater*—we find Baudelaire's attitude towards drugs. In common with most of his literary contemporaries he started taking drugs at an early age, and he belonged to the *Club des Haschichins* which used to meet at Ferdinand Boissard's room at the *Hôtel Lauzun*, but it is probable that he had little real practice in taking hashish and discontinued it after about 1845. But opium he continued to take and often to excess. What his genius owed to these drugs is difficult to estimate, but since they have the power to release what is in the subconscious mind, and tend to give extraordinary vividness of perception and sensation, magnifying every detail to larger than life size, it might be said that Baudelaire's extreme aesthetic sensibility derived in part from the use of drugs. *Le Poison, Rêve Parisien, La Vie Antérieure, Parfum Exotique*, could conceivably have been written, if not under the influence of opium, at least with the memory of the exquisite sensitivity it engenders. However that may be, the title *Les Paradis Artificiels* is significant. Baudelaire does not attempt to relate nor to compare the sensuous pleasures derived from taking opium and hashish; rather, he condemns this earthly-contrived, this fool's paradise. For he was one of the few to recognize the degradation of the human personality, the weakening of the will which opium brings about—the moral suicide, the destruction of one of man's highest faculties. It was precisely this effect that he had found so disastrous in his own case, and so too in the case of De Quincey.

Meanwhile his health was deteriorating. In 1860 he had a strange attack, something in the nature of a stroke—a first warning. The next year, syphilis came on for the third time, though he thought himself cured permanently after the second attack. He recognized the gravity of his fate and with terror foresaw the day when he would be a permanent invalid, incapable of work. Panic-stricken, he wrote to his mother: 'Now it (syphilis) has returned in a new form—discoloration of the skin, and weariness in all the joints.'

The Wings of Insanity

The next few years tell of increasing ill-health and the frequent humiliation of begging his mother for money.

At the beginning of 1862, he suffered a further attack which took a new and terrifying form. He confided in no man or woman, entrusting his secret to his diary: 'Today, the twenty-third of January, 1862, I had an ominous warning; I suddenly felt the wings of insanity brush my mind.'

In 1864, on a lecture tour in Brussels, he became so ill that he could hardly work at all. 'It is this drowsy state which makes me doubt all my faculties. At the end of three or four hours of work I am fit for nothing.'

His doctor does not seem to have understood his case, thinking it merely a nervous attack such as he had complained of for some years. Sometimes the attacks would come on at one or two in the morning, leaving him shivering with fever for six or seven hours. When he had recovered, his nerves were in a terrible state. Whenever he fixed attention on anything he developed a fear of fainting. And ever haunting and twisting his imagination was the dread of madness. He intended consulting a mental specialist on his return to Paris. Sometimes the attacks took the form of falling wherever he was, so that he only felt safe lying on his back. For the first time in his life he craved drink, because brandy gave him a temporary feeling of strength and security. By March, 1866, he was expected back in Paris, but still he did not come, for when paying a farewell visit to the Church of Saint-Loup at Namur, he staggered and fell to the ground. Though he was soon on his feet again, he was far from well during the next few days, complaining of stiffness and difficulty in moving and writing. On March 22, 1866, he had a stroke which left him paralysed on the right side, and for a while he lost the power of speech. After a fortnight in a nursing home and two and a half months' convalescence in a hotel, he had recovered sufficiently to return to Paris. He made the journey in a private railway carriage hired by the generosity of his friends to spare him the prying glances of the curious.

Arrived in Paris he moved into his new and last home. For a year in a nursing home he watched himself dying.

By early 1867 he scarcely remembered his own name. By April he had lost the will to live. After June he left his bed no more. By August he had fallen into a state of coma, only showing by the expression of his eyes that the intellect was not entirely shattered. It was not till the last day of August, 1867, that he died in his mother's arms.

During a terrible rain-storm they laid him to rest in the Montmartre Cemetery. And so Baudelaire was gone, not the Byronic, satanic figure, the *homme fatal* that some would have us imagine him, but a man of pitiable weaknesses.

For his lost years there was not merely a wistful melancholy, for youth mis-spent, but a torturing sense of the irreparableness of the past. As the ghosts of the years rose up to taunt him, he knew remorse, the dominant note of his most mature verses, bitter remorse for a life laid waste by weakness and disease.

HONORÉ DE BALZAC (1799-1850)

High Blood Pressure and Genius

'Genius is mainly an affair of energy.'
MATTHEW ARNOLD: *Essays in Criticism*.

HOW shall we sketch our Balzac? Will a few bold strokes of the pen mould the vast proportions? Will a few telling lines paint in the significant traits of character? How does the mind's eye fancy him? Is it a Friar Tuck figure in the monkish, girdled habit which it amused him to wear while writing? Is it Balzac the lover, changing his mistresses as often as he changed his coat, or is it Balzac defying the snows and his own failing health to make the arduous journey to the Ukraine to beg Mme de Hanska's hand in marriage? Is it Balzac spending a fortune on sumptuous furnishings and hangings and on an enormous collection of feminine bric-à-brac for his house? Is it Balzac changing his sex and renting a cheap room under the name of the Widow Durand, so as to outwit the bailiffs? Or is it Balzac by flickering candlelight, hunched over his writing block, his figure casting weird shadows on the peeling walls of a damp and draughty garret, a super-abundant energy and will-power alone forcing the pen to fly over sheet after sheet of manuscript, as he allows himself barely pause to take vast quantities of coffee in a wicked black brew?

Dynamic energy controlled by iron will power—and black coffee. Here at any rate among a confusion of contradictions we find a clue to one consistent aspect of the man, his genius as it was linked to his medical history. But before following it up, we must look back over the years and see how it was that this great French novelist came to be scribbling as though his life depended on it in such uninspiring surroundings.

Honoré Balzac was born on May 20, 1799, at Tours in the department of Indres and the Loire, in the same joyful, wine-loving part of France as one of his spiritual forefathers, Rabelais. His father, Bernard François, came of a family of hard-working day-labourers or very small peasant proprietors in the full-blooded Langedoc and did not despise their true name of Balssa, or sometimes Balssas. Jovial, ambitious, restless, and with a feeling for where money was to be made, he seems to have done well for himself during the Revolution, and after some rather obscure stages in his career, which he never referred to, and after holding a position in the department of war supplies and commissariat, he became first secretary in a well-known banking house. By the age of fifty he had achieved that metamorphosis, so often depicted with insight in his son's novels—from penniless but ambitious and iron-willed peasant, to upright and respected citizen. What better could he do, then, but to take to wife the beautiful, moneyed, romantically inclined, well brought-up Anne Charlotte Laure Sallambier, daughter of one of his bank chiefs and thirty-two years his junior? Balzac's mother seems to have shown complete indifference to their second child and elder son Honoré, a lovable, good-humoured child, with soft gleaming black eyes and smiling mouth. He was nursed and cared for till the age of four by a woman from the village and then boarded out with a family of strangers and only allowed home for brief week-ends. At the age of seven he was packed off to begin his education with the Oratorian Fathers in Vendôme. He does not seem to have been happy there; discipline was monastically strict, and he often did not come home for holidays. At the age of 14 he suffered, to the vast amusement of his companions, from frequent bouts of extreme somnolence, till finally his parents grew anxious and removed him from the school. He was then sent as a day boy to the *Collège* of Tours, and when, three years later, his father's business brought him and the family to Paris, Honoré studied there under a Monsieur Lepitre, an old family friend, before going to the Sorbonne to study law.

Though in his boyhood Balzac got on well with his father —they were of similar constitution and outlook—his relations with his mother lacked joy and affection. What a pitiful cry it is we find in one of his letters: 'I never had a mother!'

The appointed period of study and of apprenticeship in a notary's and a solicitor's office passed by, and Balzac was expected to find himself a suitably secure and rewarding position, eventually to marry one of wealth and good standing, to make his way socially and professionally as a respected and successful citizen, and of course bring honour to his family.

The Fire of Revolt

But a sudden fire of revolt flamed in the hitherto jovial, easy-going Balzac. For the first time he opposed the will of his family and announced his intention of gaining freedom, independence, wealth, and renown by becoming a writer.

One can imagine the impact of this announcement on his family, this union of highly respected Sallambier and hardworking, money-careful Balssa, now Balzac. That Honoré, who had never yet produced a well composed essay or a poem, nor indeed shown any sign of literary talent, should take to the doubtful calling of writer, was unthinkable! And what guarantee was there of success, or more important, of security? Argument, threat, blandishment were for a long time of no avail, then slowly, Balzac father, who had a strain of the adventurer in him, said, 'Well, why not try?' and it was decided that Honoré should have an allowance of 120 francs a month for a trial period of two years.

So we find him moving to Paris and installing himself and a few possessions in the rue Lesdiguières, in an attic at the top of five unsteady flights of stairs—the allowance was too meagre for anything better—ready to begin writing. But what would he write about? What *genre* would he adopt? Till now this practical question had not arisen! Rather ambitiously, he decided on an historical drama in verse—*Cromwell*. Immediately this was settled, vast, previously unsuspected and unharnessed energies became concentrated on the work in hand; and this was his method of work throughout his life—no sooner had pen touched paper than dynamic forces within him were released, and the vast brain contrived characters, situations, descriptions, conversations, and commentaries on them all, faster than the fleetest pen could record them. The output of energy, the concentration required to maintain it must have been tremendous, and the nervous strain would have wrecked one of less robust constitution. The only stimulation he allowed himself was black coffee—but that in gargantuan quantities. The only recreation he allowed himself—because it cost nothing—was a stroll in the fresh air. Though the two trial years were a failure, for *Cromwell*, politely acclaimed when read before a few friends and relatives, found no publisher; while two attempted novels remained but fragments—bitter years of scraping and slaving as they were, they gave him opportunity to observe man, as manifested in the life, sordid or gay, cynical or happy-go-lucky, of the poorer quarters of Paris, and to digest and correlate his observations.

'I understood these people's ways, I espoused their way of life, I felt their rags on my shoulders, I walked with my feet in their tattered shoes; their desires and their distress penetrated my soul, or my soul passed into theirs. . . . With them I flew into a passion at the employers who tyrannised over them. . . . I entertained myself by giving up my own habits, by transmuting myself into somebody else in a kind of intoxication of my moral forces. . . . I knew well the importance to me of this Faubourg, this seminary of revolutions, with its heroes, its inventors, its men of practical wisdom, its rogues and criminals, its virtues and vices, all hemmed in by misery, subdued by poverty, steeped in wine and ruined by brandy. You cannot possibly imagine what innumerable adventures unfold themselves unnoticed in this city of pain, what swiftly forgotten dramas!'

Literary Prostitution

The two years were within two months of being over, without Balzac having shown any sign of real talent nor having earned so much as a franc for himself, when suddenly the tempter, in the guise of an attractive, presentable young man with the aristocratic-sounding name of Auguste le Poitevin de l'Egreville, whispered in his ear the secret of making gold flow from the apparently unproductive pen. They would go into partnership together, he winningly suggested, Balzac turning out novels as fast as he could and Auguste finding the publisher and market for them. So Balzac moved into the family's house in the Parisian suburb of Villeparisis. Several years of literary prostitution followed, when sensational, blood-and-thunder novelettes flew off the printing press and vanished as fast on an ephemeral market. Apart from noting that as before it was a preternatural, superabundant energy which drove this human machine along without respite, aided only by still fiercer brews of coffee, let us draw a veil over these years which do neither the man nor the artist credit.

As an artist and as a man Balzac matured late, and artist and man developed simultaneously under the same influence. 'I have only two passionate desires—love and fame. Neither has found fulfilment', he said during these years. It was only in his later twenties that the conscience of the artist stirred in him to tell him how he was degrading his real self. After years of drudgery he was neither known nor respected in the world of letters, nor had he nurtured and developed his talents. As a man he had allowed himself no opportunity to mature; boxed up in his garret or in his study-bedroom in Villeparisis, he at first had neither the inclination to seek relaxation or friends, nor the money to ask even the poorest *grisette* to supper; and when he could later spare the money he was overcome with a peculiar shyness. For strange to relate, the bragging Balzac of later years was extremely shy in his youth—a shyness born not so much of weakness, perhaps, as of a sense that he knew not how to deal with the potential forces that were his to such excess. So he avoided contact with men—and with women. He speaks of a 'stage of incomplete puberty that was inordinately prolonged by overwork' and of a virility 'which only hesitantly put forth its green shoots'. Nor is it surprising that he received but scant encouragement from women, for he neglected his personal appearance no less than he abused his talents. Stockily built, with short legs, broad shoulders, a bull-neck, thick, almost negroid lips, decaying teeth, and a thick greasy mane of black hair, the fleshy face with its greasy skin and broad, indeterminate, characterless features belied the vitality of the man; only the small black eyes were alert, intense. The frequently unshaven chin, badly cut clothes, and untied shoe-laces did little to enhance the picture.

Desire Awakens

The de Berny family were good friends and near neighbours of the Balzacs in Villeparisis and in Paris. Soon after settling in Villeparisis Balzac started coaching one of the boys and gradually spent more and more time at their house. Mme de Berny was the mother of nine children, and a grandmother too, and for a woman of her age—she was forty-five—to arouse the passion of a young man would be unusual. Balzac found in her the mother's tenderness denied him by his own mother. From his mother he had heard only talk of investments, securities, and social gossip, with never an interest in his work or ambitions. In Mme de Berny was one who gently tutored the awkward young man in the social graces. Gradually she gave him confidence in himself, releasing inward tensions, arousing an awareness of a need for an understanding spirit to guide and refine his powers. She little guessed, as she encouraged his self-reliance, what demonic forces she was letting loose. As

not long before in the history of French literature Mme
Warens took Jean Jacques Rousseau under her roof merely
to tutor and guide incipient and unpolished genius, only
to find that affectionate pupil had turned to lover, so
Mme de Berny discovered in the shy and docile Balzac
that affection and admiration had, by her own doing,
turned to desire. Though she resisted him for some time,
Balzac, because it was his first love affair and because he
needed a decisive victory to maintain his newly found self-
confidence, brooked no refusal. Their intimacy lasted ten
years.

Balzac's relationship with Mme de Berny holds a two-
fold significance. Not only did she liberate the man and
the artist in him, but she determined the type of woman
with whom he would ever afterwards fall in love. Not for
him the young, attractive woman. Always did he look for
social and spiritual distinction, for sympathy and intellectual compassion, for the understanding and interest
denied him by his mother. He had to look up to the
woman he loved because of her greater experience, and
she was usually older than he. *La femme abandonnée* and
La femme de trente ans were not merely titles of his novels;
they were the heroines of his life—mature women disappointed in life and love.

Balzac had found himself as a man and as an artist.
Long since he had recognized his capacity for work, and
though years of literary prostitution had obscured his
ultimate goal, he now for the first time felt the need to
create something worthy of his talents. Breaking with de
l'Egreville, he went to visit an old friend and veteran of
the campaign against the Chouans, or Royalist Breton
rebels, and after careful research and months of intensive
and painstaking composition—for once in his life Balzac
refused to be hurried—*Le Dernier Chouan*, an historical
novel after the style of Walter Scott, was published in
1829. Its success was not overwhelming, for the sensa-
tionalism of the plot and a more than occasional slovenliness belonged still to his hack-writing days. It was not
often in fact that he managed entirely to shake himself

free of these faults. However, *Physiologie du Mariage* shortly afterwards evoked much discussion in Parisian literary circles and was an instant success.

Success

Success, however, brought no respite from work, for the artistic conscience once awakened hungrily sought fulfilment—and moreover, Balzac's passion, which he had hitherto been unable to indulge, for sumptuous furniture, antiques, paintings, miniatures, china, glassware, and trinkets of all kinds, spirited away his money. He insisted on payment in advance, so that barely was the title written than the whole novel was mortgaged. Paradoxically, the greater were his earnings, the deeper he plunged himself into debts; and the more he boasted of his enormous fees, the higher grew the pile of unpaid bills.

The impact of Balzac on Parisian high society following his literary success was disappointing. His awkward figure, coarse features, overpowering personality, undisciplined exuberance, and untidiness made him the butt of the cartoonist and the object of suppressed sniggers. Yet though he realized that he could never cut the figure of society lion, high society held him fascinated. It was a naïve *snobbisme*, another of those traits of the *nouveau riche* which he could so acidly depict in his novels, which made him affect the ways of society, to the extent of prefixing an aristocratic 'de' to his name and to claiming descent from the d'Entrague family and having their arms engraved on his cutlery and painted on his carriage. Though truth to tell, the eternally plebeian Balzac would have appeared more natural in shirt sleeves and apron behind the bar of a sun-baked, southern *bistro*. But it was his magnanimity, which held him aloof from society's meannesses and pettiness.

How magnificently he paints this society, even as he breathes life into the scenes of the poorer quarters of Paris. For Balzac could penetrate the secrets of any milieu and ruthlessly unearth its foibles, just as he revealed the secrets of men's hearts, lay bare those weaknesses and strengths, ambitions, fears, vices, virtues, and secret, unacknowledged motives, which are the activating forces of their lives. Balzac was an observer of the pageant of life, an historian of his own time. In everything he saw he found his raw material; it was his genius that charged it with an inward, essential dynamic. No one better than Balzac illustrates the words of Dr. Johnson when he speaks of 'Genius, that energy which collects, combines, amplifies, and animates'. It was clear that the variety of themes and backgrounds to be drawn upon were infinite; to keep them within bounds Balzac had to have a plan to work to, to become a 'Walter Scott plus un architecte'. Gradually the concept of the *Comèdie Humaine*—an earthly parallel to the *Divina Comedia*—became formulated into an epic of contemporary life in all its aspects. The work is classified into scenes from private life, provincial life, Parisian life, political, military, and country life, and philosophical studies. To link these various aspects into some kind of unity, many of the 2000 characters appear in more than one novel.

L'Etranger

If only time and peace of mind to work out the great scheme were granted him! But there were still interminable arguments with publishers and printers. Society imposed its own obligations on his time. His passion for lavish spending was insatiable and involved him in huge debts. More than once he had to remove his valuables to secret hide-outs to escape the hands of the bailiffs. Disastrously he ventured into the publishing business, into speculation in Sardinian silver mines, even into politics. He was harassed on every side. And when a letter bearing a Russian stamp and signed *L'Etranger* arrived, how could he know it was to start a love affair that was to cause him more hopes, anguish, and disillusionment than was in him to bear? For in Mme de Hanska, the sender of the letter, whom he met the following year in 1833, he had found the woman he wanted to marry. She promised to be his wife as soon as her ageing and failing husband died. There was a strenuous journey to the Ukraine, there were brief meetings in foreign capitals, and there was a voluminous correspondence. But when the black-edged envelope finally announced her husband's death at the end of 1840, Mme de Hanska's affections seemed to have grown cold. She delayed till the end of her mourning; she put off till after her daughter's wedding; she hesitated with innumerable excuses. When finally in 1850 she consented to become his wife, she knew that Balzac was already on his death bed.

Balzac's Case-History

The usual childhood measles and mumps do not seem to have come Balzac's way. The broad shoulders and chest indicated enormous physical strength, and though his late development and obesity might betray some ductless-gland imbalance, till his thirties he enjoyed excellent health in spite of the strain he imposed on himself. It was in 1834 that he first suffered from a slight brain congestion, with sensations of losing his balance or being 'off the vertical'. This went unheeded till it was repeated two years later. His physician Dr Nacquart diagnosed arachnitis, or inflammation of the arachnoid—the central of the three meninges which cover the brain.

1837 was a year of disasters. His sister fell ill and her husband was in financial difficulties; his young brother Henry, a ne'er-do-well who had been sent to do what he might in India, returned now, penniless with a wife fifteen years his senior. He owed money all round—not that that was a novel situation for Balzac, but he was also in arrears with work; he was harassed by court proceedings and by exacting and unscrupulous publishers. Mme de

Berny was too ill with heart trouble to give her usual comfort, and later that year she died. In life she had awakened Balzac's genius and manhood; in her death she killed his youth. He began to feel the weight of his years and to wonder for the first time whether his strength—that energy and vitality wherein lay the secret of his success and which he had so long taken for granted—would last to the completion of the *Comédie Humaine*. In these years he was producing some of his greatest works, most of them falling within the framework of the *Comédie Humaine: La femme de trente ans* (1831–32), *Eugénie Grandet* (1833), *Le père Goriot* (1834), *Grandeur et décadence de César Birotteau* (1837), *Le médecin de campagne* (1833), to mention but a few. But the puffy cheeks, the sallow complexion, the double chin, and the flabby body betokened endless nights spent at work behind curtained windows, and lack of exercise and fresh air. No wonder, then, that even this mighty frame began to weaken. There were nervous twitchings of the eyes which he feared might indicate the beginning of some nervous disease. Over-indulgence in strong black coffee brought its revenge in stomach cramps. More serious, he began to suffer from symptoms indicative of high blood pressure: pains and fullness in the head, attacks of giddiness, flushings, inability to concentrate; as he no longer reacted to the stimulus of coffee, this was the most serious from the point of view of his work. He began to have bouts of unbelievable tiredness, followed by hours of death-like sleep—he who had been able to work eighteen hours at a stretch without feeling exhausted.

It is doubtful if any of the known ductless glands of the body play a primary part in the genesis of high blood pressure (hypertension), though hypertension is frequently associated with endocrine (ductless gland) disorders and may, in fact, be the first evidence of such a disorder. Physicians also recognize that stress on that very small, but highly romantic, area at the base of the brain, the hypothalamus, may affect the pituitary and the adrenal glands. It is now generally accepted that hypertension is not caused by sustained overactivity of the nervous system, but that in certain types of individuals an hereditary or constitutional factor plays an important rôle. They are usually short-set persons, with a short thick neck, often with a high colour—the plethoric or full-blooded, capable, and energetic individual. Balzac clearly falls into this category. It is possible that an endocrine imbalance was connected with his high blood pressure, but on this point one cannot be dogmatic. Dr Nacquart, a lifelong friend who had been more than generous to him in times of financial crisis, diagnosed hypertrophy of the left ventricle of the heart—a condition caused by the persistent demand for extra work imposed on it by the increased pressure of the blood.

About 1840 Dr Nacquart found that his patient had hepatitis—inflammation of the liver—for which he prescribed Seltz water mixed with sweetened vinegar. Hours of writing by candle-light also took their toll, resulting in serious eye strain.

By 1844 Balzac was complaining of an irresistible lethargy. His facial muscles would spasmodically contract, and he had headaches and nervous twitchings of the eyes. The symptoms increased in severity with the years till in 1848 the stomach pains became intolerable.

But worse than the physical sufferings were the sufferings of his soul, the spiritual fatigue, the *ennui*. 'Je souffre physiquemeht de quelque chose dans l'âme, qui se dilate . . .', he complained.

Much of his spiritual and mental weariness may be attributed to the unnatural situation which had grown up between Mme de Hanska and himself. Between 1834 and 1841 they never saw each other but kept up a correspondence. Though passion had died in each, neither wished to break off relations altogether. Mme de Hanska, because her pride in the humble devotion of the great novelist had become the most important thing in her life, and she was loath to abandon a correspondence which so flattered her vanity. Balzac, because he could not do without the habit of self-display which had become second nature to him. When news of Monsieur de Hanska's death reached Balzac, he felt a sudden relief of tension and a resurgence of his former love. But Mme de Hanska was in no hurry to marry him. For one thing she was well aware of his intimacies with other women, and she was jealous. Who knows what other reasons this strange, frivolous woman may have contrived for herself? In any case it seems certain that her shallow nature was incapable of love on Balzac's level.

Balzac knew that only by plunging himself into his work could he find any peace of mind over these years. As he followed out the destinies of his characters, they became more real to him than the physical world around him. Despite failing concentration, eye-strain, and nervous twitchings, an enormous output was maintained—*Les illusions perdues* (1837–43), *Ursule Mirouet* (1841), *Une ténébreuse affaire* (1841), *Le cure de village* (1839–46), *Les paysans* (1844).

In the autumn of 1846 Balzac was summoned to the Ukraine. With what eagerness did he make the difficult journey to Wierzchownia, 'across a quarter of the earth'. But as a son of Touraine he was unused to Russian winters and succumbed there to bronchitis, which left no doubt as to the state of his heart. Upon leaving his sick-bed, he gasped for breath at every step and found even talking an effort. It was not till 1850 that Mme de Hanska, in the certainty that he had little time left to live, consented to marry him. On March 14, at the Church of St Barbara in the Ukranian town of Berdichev, they were married very quietly.

The journey back to Paris was a nightmare. On the Polish border Balzac was overcome by extreme weakness; he lost his appetite and kept breaking out in profuse perspiration. As they reached Dresden he was in a state of complete exhaustion and half blind. When at last they came to Paris and he led his bride into the house he had prepared for her, Balzac was coming home to die. His eyesight had failed completely.

When the end came late on the evening of August 17,

1850, his wife had retired, and it was only his aged mother who was there to comfort him dying.

So the great Honoré de Balzac slipped away from life. The *Comédie Humaine* was left unfinished. One might wish that he had not driven himself by excessive work and activity to an untimely death at the age of fifty-one from a diseased heart. Yet had he not goaded himself on so frenziedly he would never have amassed the wealth of observed detail and experience in which his work is so rich, and certainly we should not have seen the completion of so much of the *Comédie Humaine* as we have. In whom else in the annals of literature was combined the breadth of vision to conceive so vast an epic, the attention to detail to make it live before us; the courage to undertake and to continue; the physical strength to transform the vision to reality?

JOHN KEATS (1795–1821)

Tuberculosis and Genius

> ' When I have fears that I may cease to be
> Before my pen has glean'd my teeming
> brain. . . .'

'I KNOW the colour. . . . That drop of blood is my death warrant!' One bitter wintery evening of early 1820 Keats rode without an overcoat on the outside of the Hampstead coach and arrived, chilled, at Wentworth Place, the home of his close friend Charles Armitage Brown. As Brown hurried him to bed he heard him cough, then saw him examine the bright red spot that had appeared on the white sheet. 'After regarding it stead-fastly', Brown relates, 'he looked up in my face with a calmness of countenance I shall never forget.' How reveal-ing are Brown's words! Keats calm at that awful moment —and he was not by nature a placid man—suggests that the dramatic appearance of that stain of blood—con-sumption's visiting card—came to him not entirely as a surprise, that he may have had a presentiment, an inkling that his untimely and tragic end was not so far off, was in fact only a twelve-month distant. Indeed, as we shall see later, the numerous allusions to death in his poetry bear this out. For he had studied medicine; he had seen first his mother and then his brother succumb to the very same disease. He must have read in the unequivocal message of that drop of blood only a confirmation of his own, perhaps unacknowledged, misgivings.

. . . . . .

In 1810, Keats's mother, gay, charming, indulgent, imprudent Frances Jennings, a widow since Thomas Keats's fatal fall from a horse six years before, remarried, speedily but disastrously, to a Mr Rawlings, and returned now to her mother's house, was dying slowly from tuberculosis of the lungs. The young Keats, a healthy, boisterous, impressionable schoolboy, spent a good part of his time at her bedside, nursing her in the last stages of her illness, witnessing her last painful breaths. The emotional upset, brought about earlier by the shock of his father's death, was renewed and sharpened, too, by the particular circumstances of the relationship existing between mother and son. A discerning biographer notes that the influence of his mother's death on the evolution of Keats's genius has not been adequately appreciated; for from this date Keats became engrossed in literature. He read avidly, exhausting his school library, and before long, from steeping himself in literature, he was moved to creating it, recapturing the music of Spencer in his first laborious verses, timidly but joyfully experimenting with this gift he suddenly found within him. His schoolmasters merely noticed that his intellectual powers were developing apace towards a precocious maturity.

The next few years of the poet's life can be briefly chronicled, as they have little bearing on our present theme. Some twelve months after the mother's death, the grandmother Jennings, finding the responsibility of four grandchildren falling heavily upon her, appointed as guardian an old friend Richard Abbey, a coffee and tea merchant in the City of London. Discovering the eldest boy John unsuited to a business career in his own firm, he decided to apprentice him to an Edmonton surgeon, Thomas Hammond. John apparently made no objection. With his exceptional mental qualities he seems to have progressed satisfactorily during his apprenticeship. However, before the customary five years were over, Hammond and he quarrelled for some reason unknown to us. Whether the surgeon regarded his pupil as 'An idle, loafing fellow, always writing poetry'—the opinion expressed by one of his fellow-students—or whether the pupil tired of the eternal drug-grinding, plaster-spreading, and bleeding, they agreed to break the indentures. On October 2, 1815, Keats, being then in his twentieth year, entered Guy's Hospital, and in July of the following year passed with ease and credit the final examination of Apothecary's Hall and was licensed to practise medicine.

He had been an industrious and intelligent, but not an outstanding, student. Not always had he been able to give his entire attention to lectures, for at times 'there came a sunbeam into the room, and with it a whole troop of creatures floating in the ray; and I was off with them to Oberon and fairyland'. Whether medicine now lost one of its potentially great we cannot say, but certain it is that when, having successfully cleared the first hurdle along a career in medicine, Keats put away his medical books and surgical instruments and decided to follow the muse 'on the viewless wings of Poesie', English literature gained one of its greatest and noblest figures.

A thing of beauty is a joy for ever

In spite of busy apprentice and student days, attending lectures, taking notes, operating, and cramming for his examination, Keats's poetic genius had been slowly developing. Sitting in the window-seat, which soon became known as 'Keats's place', in his lodging over a tallow-chandler's shop in St. Thomas's Street, he would capture in words some of the fleeting imagery in his brain, and among some early and immature verses, penned a few immortal lines. Thus, one evening, while the others were studying their text-books and lecture-notes, sitting in his favourite place and letting his mind roam through space and time to strange haunts of magic and beauty, he composed a line as exquisite as any in the language and as imperishable as the language itself. Turning to Henry Stephens (who is remembered for having introduced creosote into medicine), he recited 'A thing of beauty is a joy for ever'.

'What think you of that?' he asked, and Stephens replied, 'That it will live for ever'.

The four years after Keats's break with medicine are considered his most productive. The year 1817 witnessed the publication of his first book—a small collection of poems written during his student days, immature for the most part but including the sonnet 'On first looking into Chapman's Homer', which contains lines of incomparable grandeur and haunting beauty. It is intriguing to find that the young poet, like the mature Wordsworth at a later date, was fond of long, trivial, and pedantically cumbersome titles for some of his poems, such as 'On receiving a curious shell, and a copy of verses, from the same ladies'. The biting reviews of *Endymion* in two of the contemporary magazines hurt Keats's sensitive heart deeply, but the suggestion that they precipitated his early death is sentimental and unscientific nonsense. The year 1819, in which were published *The Eve of St. Agnes* and *La Belle Dame sans Merci*, has been called his *annus mirabilis*.

In his eagerness to taste that ripeness and maturity that might add to the stature of his poetic muse, while on a visit to Oxford in September, 1817, Keats contracted syphilis—a point on which his biographers tend to be reticent. For a few weeks he kept to the house, taking mercury, and he was able to report that this drug had 'corrected the poison and improved my health'.

The Spectre of Consumption

Once more the spectre of consumption raised its head and slowly claimed a second victim in the family. Again it fell to John to nurse his brother Tom, now in an advanced stage of tuberculosis, through the summer of 1818, uncertain whether he could leave him to join his friend Brown in a walking tour of the western highlands. He did in fact go. The trip involved strenuous exercise, poor weather conditions, uncertain food and lodging over a longish period, and Keats complained of a sore throat which finally forced him to abandon the tour. The malady which was to cut off his career in the springtime of life, leaving so tragically rich a promise, had begun to show its hand. Returning to Hampstead John found Tom in an alarming condition. He died on December 1 of that year.

Keats was but five feet in height, yet broad of shoulder.

JOHN KEATS
(1795–1821)

There was something indefinably majestic about this little man, which made women passing him in the street look back and desire him to be taller. His face was long and sensitive, his dark-hazel eyes were glowing with life as though they were gazing on some sight unutterably lovely; his mouth was full and rather pugnacious. His voice was low, grave, and hauntingly rich. So far he had been normally healthy. However, it now seems beyond doubt that the disease had already established itself in the lungs, even though it gave rise to no suspicious symptoms. For it would have been impossible for Keats to have stayed so long by his mother's and his brother's bedside without being infected. Moreover, the first symptom which troubled him was the sore throat which came on during the Highland tour. Tuberculosis rarely occurs primarily in the throat; the tubercle bacilli probably passed from the lungs into the larynx, setting up a localized infection in the throat.

These conjectures can be made in the light of modern medical knowledge. Did it cross Keats's mind that he was marked down as the next victim?

Certainly, during these years when he reached full maturity, between the time of Tom's illness and his own first haemorrhage, he seems to have been preoccupied with the idea of death. *Lamia* finishes with the eerie and tragic death of the two lovers. In *Isabella* the death of Lorenzo has a gruesome twist. After the joyous flight of the young lovers in the delicate and lovely *The Eve of St. Agnes*, we read:

> 'Angela the old
> Died palsy-twitch'd, with meagre face deform;
> The Beadsman, after thousand aves told,
> For aye unsought for, slept among his ashes cold.'

In the *Ode to a Nightingale* are the lines:

> 'Darkling I listen; and, for many a time
> I have been half in love with easeful Death,
> Call'd him soft names in many a mused rhyme,
> To take into the air my quiet breath ;
> Now more than ever seems it rich to die,
> To cease upon the midnight with no pain.'

And in one of his sonnets the idea of untimely death becomes clearly formulated:

> 'When I have fears that I may cease to be
> Before my pen has glean'd my teeming brain . . .
> When I behold upon the night's starr'd face,
> Huge cloudy symbols of a high romance,
> And think that I may never live to trace
> Their shadows, with the magic hand of chance . . .'

Contrasting with, and serving to intensify in Keats's mind, the frustration of death were two ideas: first, the immortality of the poet. Personifying Poesy in the eternal song of the Nightingale he cries:

> 'Thou wast not born for death, immortal Bird!'

Secondly, the immutability of the one thing he lived to serve, Beauty:

> 'Cold Pastoral!
> When old age shall this generation waste,
> Thou shalt remain, in midst of other woe
> Than ours, a friend to man, to whom thou say'st,
> "Beauty is truth, truth beauty,"—that is all
> Ye know on earth, and all ye need to know.'
> (*Ode on a Grecian Urn.*)

One circumstance in his private life, the dream of happiness with the girl to whom he was engaged, made unbearable antithesis with the certainty of early death. Frances Brawne, generally called 'Fanny', was a mere slip of a girl of seventeen, when the blind and winged archer pierced the poet's heart. She was very small and made him forget his own smallness. To Keats she became the most radiant and enchanting woman he had ever beheld, with her smiling, coquettish blue eyes, her aquiline nose, her fragile face like ivory in colour, her light brown hair waved in the latest fashion. He raised her to the stature of a goddess and worshipped at her feet. That Fanny was fond of him there can be little doubt, but she was scarcely sentimental about an invalid without money or future.

Flattered by his adulation, she was at the same time prepared to flirt with other men. When Keats realized the nearness of his last necessity, he was sufficiently manly to offer to break the engagement, yet Fanny refused to listen. Though some of his loveliest poems were the fruit of this passionate courtship, curiously enough it failed utterly to enrich his pen with ripeness and mellow understanding.

I feel the flowers growing over me

His last days Keats spent in Rome, in a tall yellow house by the steps of Sta Trinità dei Monti, in the Piazza di Spagna. He was in the medical care of Dr (afterwards Sir) James Clark, a young physician who was interested in the influence of climate on tuberculosis. The doctor found his patient rather unusual in that he exhibited none of that pathetic *spes phthisica* (the hopefulness of the consumptive) which is so characteristic a feature of the disease and which inspires him to make elaborate plans for the morning which is never to come. Keats realized only too well how desperate was his fate. 'How long will this posthumous life of mine last? . . . I feel the flowers growing over me.'

Death came peacefully on February 23, 1821, when he was but in the twenty-sixth year of his age. And when they laid to rest, among the ruins of the old Aurelian Wall in the Protestant Cemetery of Rome, his youth, his loveliness, and his unfilled dreams, Shelley, who was so soon to sleep by his side, wept for him:

'He has outsoared the shadow of our night;
Envy and calumny, and hate and pain,
And that unrest which men miscall delight,
Can touch him not and torture not again.'

Tuberculosis and Literary Genius

Some of the greatest poets and writers of prose the world has ever seen have been perfectly normal physically and mentally. Yet is it a mere coincidence that consumption has claimed so large a number of victims among literary men? That a relationship exists between tuberculous infection and literary genius is generally recognized but its nature remains obscure. It is tempting to speculate that the toxins elaborated by the tubercle bacillus paralyse the highest critical faculties localized in the cortex of the brain, with the result that the so-called 'vegetative' faculties such as imagination, rhythm, colour sense, and possibly poetry, are now free to act. We know so little, however, about the biochemistry of the tubercle bacillus, and much exact research is needed before the mystery of its action on a poet's brain can be elucidated. Certain it is that in some cases, at least, creative mental power appears to vary directly with the progress of the infection and that, as it were, there exists an alliance between fever and art.

As long as his strength allowed, John Keats reached after vertiginous heights of poetry. His later work shows at times a feverish quality, and there is little doubt that tuberculosis was responsible for the haste with which he worked, as though he felt impelled to pour out as much beauty as possible into words before the coming of the night. It was then that images would tumble so fast and furious from his brain that he has been accused of prolixity. Whether, had he lived the normal span of years, he might have bridled this exuberance and achieved yet greater things, or whether, not being fanned on by the circumstances of his life, the fires of his imagination might never have burned so brightly, no one can say. As disease gradually sapped his strength and extinguished these fires, the antithesis between aspiration and the time allotted for fulfilment became sharper and sharper, driving him to the final despair of the epitaph he penned for himself and which, dying, he desired his friend John Severn to place over his grave:

'Here lies one whose name is writ in water.'

ROBERT BURNS (1759–96)

Rheumatic Fever and Genius

> 'Then gently scan your brother man,
>   Still gentler sister woman;
> Tho' they may gang a kennin wrang,
>   To step aside is human:
>
> One point must still be greatly dark,
>   The moving why they do it;
> And just as lamely can ye mark
>   How far perhaps they rue it.'

'STRICTLY speaking, perhaps no British man has so deeply affected the thoughts and feelings of so many men, as this solitary and altogether private individual, with means apparently the humblest.' These words were written by a great Scot about a brother Scot, for they occur in Thomas Carlyle's essay on Robert Burns. Superficially, the two men were utterly dissimilar, yet they shared a fundamental spirit of revolt against religious, political, and social anachronisms.

Is it possible, even at this distance of time, to write dispassionately of one who in his own lifetime created his own legend? A legend that has outdistanced the man and has shaped an Olympian setting, against which our emotional response continues to synchronize in strangely theatrical unreality with the frozen silence, the wild cadences of the howling storm, the infinite charm of the purple heather, the unattainable majesty of the misty mountains. Is it possible, when writing of the human frailties of Robert Burns, to cultivate a mind innocent of cherished illusions or of deep-rooted prejudices?

Robert Burns was born in a humble, two-roomed thatched cottage in Ayrshire, on January 25, 1759. His father, William Burnes or Burness, had worked as a gardener near Edinburgh before he became gardener and overseer of a small estate on the banks of the Doon, where he also leased a few acres of land for his own use. The father was a man of strong individuality, but Robert, the eldest of seven children, was much more like his mother in temperament. Uneducated in the conventional sense of the term, she was a woman of keen intelligence, and it was from her that the boy inherited his imaginative qualities. As he was more akin to his mother in appearance and character, so was he nearer to her in his love for the tales and the poems in which she delighted.

William Burnes, an enlightened man, joined with a few neighbours in engaging a young itinerant teacher to instruct their children. In 1766 the family moved to the farm of Mount Oliphant, but the boy continued to attend the schoolroom at Alloway for a further two years. Though his subsequent education was erratic and desultory, of education in the wider sense he received much more than these brief periods of schooling would suggest. He also showed a precocious interest in his father's collection of books, the first two works he read being lives of Hannibal and of William Wallace. In time he could read French with facility, but his knowledge of Latin never got beyond the rudimentary stage. Delving into Pope's writings, he became an assiduous scribbler at the age of twelve. He loved Shakespeare and greatly enjoyed a collection of English songs. These he would go over 'verse by verse, carefully noting the tender and sublime from affectation and fustian'.

The Seeds of Disease

Though he was allowed such glimpses of the treasure-house of story, song, and verse, his opportunities for dallying amid their delights were necessarily circumscribed. Ill-fortune seemed to dog every enterprise undertaken by William Burnes, and from his fourteenth year Robert was called upon to do the work of a grown ploughman. While his father was unsuccessfully attempting to wring a living from the farm at Mount Oliphant and later at Lochlea, the boy's life combined 'the gloom of a hermit with the toil of a galley slave'.

The distinguished psychiatrist Sir James Crichton-Browne believed that the exposure and overwork to which Burns was subjected at this early age sowed the seeds of the disease which brought about his untimely death. In a little book entitled *Burns From a New Point of View*, he expressed the opinion that from boyhood the poet suffered from endocarditis, which he defines as a 'disease of the substance and lining membrane of the heart with the origination of which alcohol had nothing to do'. He accumulated an impressive array of evidence to show that Burns was, for his day, a moderate drinker. Burns was unfortunate in his first biographer, James Currie, a physician who was also a fanatical teetotaller and who had much sympathy for the poet, but not for the man. The bias in this work was not taken into account by some later writers, Carlyle among them, and undue stress has ever since been laid upon Burns's fondness for drink and women. In Sir James Crichton-Browne's view, there are sufficient allusions to the characteristic and distressing symptoms of endocarditis in the poet's correspondence to put the diagnosis beyond reasonable doubt. Lockhart mentions hearing from one 'who often shared his bed with him at Mossgiel, that even at that early period, when intemperance assuredly had had nothing to do with the matter, those ominous symptoms of radical disorder in the digestive system . . . were so regularly his nocturnal visitants, that it was his custom to have a great tub of cold water by his bedside into which he usually plunged more than once in the course of the night, thereby procuring instant, though but short-lived relief'. At the risk of being accused of resurrecting a trivial anecdote, one is tempted to repeat the story that one night in Burns's infancy the roof of the cottage blew off and mother and child had to be carried through the Atlantic gale to find shelter in a neighbour's house. It is notorious that, though rheumatic fever is essentially a disease of later childhood, its origin can often be looked for very early in infancy. The infant's heart is peculiarly susceptible to the toxins of rheumatism.

As Burns reached early manhood he began to give expression to the idealism and sentimentality which was to permeate his writings. At sixteen, he wrote his first song, 'Handsome Nell', a tribute to a girl he met in the harvest-field. In 1782 he entered into partnership with a flax-dresser at Irvine, but though he gained some valuable experience of men and affairs, the business failed. William Burnes died of consumption on February 13, 1784. The lack of success in farming Mount Oliphant had been repeated at Lochlea, and three months before their father's death, Robert and his brother Gilbert had taken the farm of Mossgiel. Together with two sisters they strove for four years to win a living from the bleak, unproductive soil.

During these days of unremitting toil Robert composed many of his most touching verses as he drove the plough, committing them to paper when the day's work was done. The beautiful poem to the *Mountain Daisy* arose from the sight of this dainty flower in the path of his plough. When the prospects at Mossgiel seemed hopeless, Burns thought of trying to obtain a post on a plantation in the West Indies. He showed something of his feelings in the famous lines to *The Mouse*, the exquisitely tender apology for demolishing the small creature's home:

> 'But Mousie, thou art no thy lane
> In proving foresight may be vain:
> The best-laid schemes o' mice an' men
>   Gang aft agley,
> An' lea's us nought but grief an' pain,
>   For promis'd joy!
>
> Still thou art blest, compar'd wi' me!
> The present only toucheth thee:
> But och! I backward cast my e'e,
>   On prospects drear!
> An' forward, tho' I canna see,
>   I guess an' fear!'

The Poetic Genius Flourishes

Though his years on the land had been unprofitable, his poetic genius had flourished. *The Holy Fair*, the *Twa Herds*, and *Holy Willie's Prayer*, were scathing satires against self-righteousness and intolerance. His tilting at the hypocrisy of certain members of the Kirk was held by some to be impious, but time has shown that his exposure of their shortcomings was a service to the Christian Church. Though he won the plaudits of his Ayrshire contemporaries by assailing the 'unco guid', Burns was neither atheist nor materialist. In the *Cottar's Saturday Night*, in which he portrayed his father as the pious cottar, he drew a comparison between simple devotion and hypocrisy:

> 'Compar'd with this, how poor Religion's pride,
> In all the pomp of method, and of art;
> When men display to congregations wide
> Devotion's ev'ry grace, except the heart!'

Offered a post as plantation manager in the West Indies, Burns began to consider how to raise the money for his passage. His brother Gilbert suggested that it might be done by printing his poems, and acting on this advice Robert went to a Kilmarnock printer. Three hundred subscribers were obtained, and an edition of six hundred copies was published in the autumn of 1786. Copies of this Kilmarnock edition have changed hands for sums running into four figures; Burns was well content when its sales brought him about £20. It contained more than enough to establish the poet's reputation for all time, bearing on every page the imprint of genius. Not only did the poems impress by their technical excellence, but they made it manifest that in the young farmer Scotland possessed a bard whose work had more of the vital human spark than could be found in that of any of his pre-decessors. The poems won the approbation of his country-men because their topicality and outspokenness made them the most effective attack ever launched against political injustices and the abuse of privilege. Burns, however, did more than wage war on those of whom he disapproved, for like Carlyle, he stressed the dignity of labour:

> 'Is there for honest Poverty
>   That hangs his head, an' a' that;
> The coward slave—we pass him by,
>   We dare by poor for a' that!
> For a' that, an' a' that,
>   Our toils obscure an' a' that,
> The rank is but the guinea stamp,
>   The Man's the gowd for a' that.
>
> What though on hamely fare we dine,
>   Wear hoddin grey, an' a' that;
> Gie fools their silks, and knaves their wine,
>   A man's a Man for a' that:
> For a' that, an' a' that,
>   Their tinsel show, an' a' that;
> The honest man, tho' e'er sae poor,
>   Is king o' men for a' that.'

These sentiments which Burns held throughout his life explain much of the melancholy so often remarked upon by those who knew him. When his status was firmly established after the success of the Kilmarnock edition, he frequently had cause to reflect on the advantages of birth and education:

'Poverty! thou half sister of death, thou cousin-german of hell! Oppressed by thee, the man of sentiment, whose heart glows with independence, and melts with sensibility, inly pines under the neglect, or writhes in bitterness of soul, under the contumely of arrogant, unfeeling wealth. Oppressed by thee, the son of genius, whose ill-starred ambition plants him at the tables of the fashionable and polite, must see, in suffering silence, his remark neglected, and his person despised, while shallow greatness, in his idiot attempts at wit, shall meet with countenance and applause.'

A Case-History

That symptoms of the disease which brought the poet to an early grave dated from boyhood is shown by a statement of his brother Gilbert:

'I doubt not but the hard labour and sorrow of this period of his life, was in a great measure the cause of that depression of spirits with which Robert was so often afflicted through his whole life afterwards. At this time he was most constantly afflicted in the evenings with a dull headache, which, at a future period of his life, was exchanged for a palpitation of the heart, and a threatening of fainting and suffocation in his bed, in the night-time.'

Burns was then about thirteen years of age. We know from his own pen that he was prey to a 'constitutional melancholy or hypochondriacism that made me fly solitude'. In a remarkable letter to his father in 1781/2 he referred to his health and to the sombre trend of his thoughts:

'My health is nearly the same as when you were here, only my sleep is a little sounder. . . . The weakness of my nerves has so debilitated my mind, that I dare neither review past wants, nor look forward into futurity. . . . I am quite transported at the thought, that ere long, perhaps very soon, I shall bid an eternal adieu to all the pains and uneasiness, and disquietudes of this weary life; for I assure you I am heartily tired of it; and if I do not very much deceive myself, I could contentedly and gladly resign it. . . . I foresee that poverty and obscurity probably await me. . . .'

An interesting passage occurs in a letter to Mrs Dunlop:

'I am better, but not quite free of my complaint (palpitation). . . . You must not think . . . that in my way of life, I want exercise.

Of that I have enough; but occasional hard drinking is the devil to me.'

On a previous occasion he had confessed that he 'parted with a slice of his constitution' at each excess.

Professor Dugald Stewart may be quoted in support of the statement that Burns was not a heavy drinker:

'Notwithstanding the various reports I heard during the preceding winter, of Burns's predilection for convivial, and not very select society, I should have concluded in favour of his habits of sobriety, from all of him that ever fell under my own observation. He told me indeed himself, that the weakness of his stomach was such as to deprive him entirely of any merit in his temperance. I was, however, somewhat alarmed about the effect of his now comparatively sedentary and luxurious life, when he confessed to me, the first night he spent in my house after his winter's campaign in town, that he had been much disturbed when in bed, by a palpitation at his heart, which, he said, was a complaint to which he had of late become subject.'

When he was in Edinburgh in 1787, Burns sprained his ankle and described himself as 'under the care of a surgeon, with a bruised limb extended on a cushion, and the tints of my mind vying with the livid horrors preceding a midnight thunderstorm'. It was at this period that the famous surgeon, Alexander Wood ('Lang Sandy Wood'), who had heard his patient express the wish for an excise appointment, approached one of the commissioners, with the result that Burns's name was put on the roll. In August of the following year the poet wrote: 'I fear my knee will never be entirely well', and it may be surmised that, as his trouble had thus lasted more than a year, the original injury had localized the rheumatic infection in the knee, from which it extended to other parts of the body. In those days the medical profession failed to appreciate the tragic relationship between rheumatic fever and heart disease. Some of Burns's letters during that period make pathetic reading. 'My constitution and frame', he wrote to his friend, Alexander Cunningham, on February 25,

ROBERT BURNS
(1759–96)

1794, 'were *ab origine*, blasted with a deep incurable taint of hypochondria, which poisons my existence', and on January 31, 1796: 'I became a victim of a most severe rheumatic fever, and long the die spun doubtful until after many weeks of sick bed it seems to have turned up life, and I am beginning to crawl across my room.' It was a few days later, when he had only just started to be up and about, that he attended a tavern dinner in convivial company. The party broke up in the small hours of the morning, and the poet, slightly intoxicated, fainted in the cold air and lay asleep for some hours in the snow. His rheumatism now returned with renewed vigour: 'I close my eyes in misery and open them without hope.'

On Dr William Maxwell's advice, the poet went to the Brow-Well, a mild chalybeate spring on the Solway Firth, in order to try the effect of 'bathing, country quarters, and riding'. This unfortunate treatment aggravated his condition, and the patient sank rapidly and died on July 21, 1796. The terminal fever and delirium suggest malignant endocarditis as a complication. At the time when they were laying him in his grave, Jean Burns gave birth to a posthumous son. In Burns's final illness there were no signs and symptoms to suggest that he died of alcoholism; no hallucinations indicative of delirium tremens, no muscular cramps or paralysis of a toxic neuritis, no jaundice or dropsy spelling cirrhosis of the liver.

What of Burns the man? That he was of a passionate nature and that his relations with women were far from creditable there is no doubt. From the days of his youth into his maturity poetry and sex were inalienable twin emotions in his soul. Falling as easily, and as frequently, out of, as in, love, some of his affairs were the plaything of the idle moment; others were sentimental platonic friendships, while others again amounted simply to seduction of servant girls whose sole attraction lay in their age-old enigma of sex. In 1790, for example, when Jean Burns had returned to her home on a visit, her husband sought consolation in the arms of a blonde barmaid. The last of the poet's mistresses to bear a name, she disappeared into obscurity. Those who followed her have remained intriguingly innominate: a shadowy, mysterious, sorry train of girls who knowingly played with fire because their hearts could not say no.

Rheumatic Fever and Genius

To this day rheumatic fever remains a disease of fascinating mystery, the Sphinx and Circe of medicine. In an age of ignorance and superstition 'rheumatism' was regarded as a 'peccant humour', a 'rheum' flowing from the brain to all the other parts of the body, where it caused much pain and a host of constitutional disturbances. But the nature of this 'rheum' was entirely conjectural. All the advances in medical knowledge have done little to shed light on its enigma. Some speak of bacterial poisons permeating the tissues, even changing their chemistry; others continue to be intrigued by the possibility of the existence of a 'soil' peculiarly susceptible to the rheumatic infection. Many clinicians recognize a definite type of child as a potential victim of this crippling disease —thin, wiry, highly strung, sensitive, and always of exceptionally high intelligence. The rheumatic child was described by that great and wise paediatrician, the late Sir Frederic Still, as *par excellence* the nervous child— almost uncontrollable in its excitement over games and amusements, or, on the other hand, excessively timid and almost morbidly shy.

Robert Burns more than once refers to his 'weakness of the nerves . . . the least anxiety or perturbation in my breast produces the most unhappy effect on my whole frame'. 'Embittering remorse (the tortured note is of peculiar significance) scars my fancy at the gloomy forebodings of death. . . . I am groaning under the miseries of a diseased nervous system . . . for now three weeks I have been so ill with a nervous headache, being scarce able to lift up my head. What is man?' Is it altogether surprising that, faced with such a morbid catalogue of divers symptoms, one of the poet's physicians believed melancholy and low spirits to have been half of his patient's disease?

Conscious of Time's hungry annihilation lying in wait for him, promising freedom from pain of body and from sorrow of soul, Burns sought and found escape equally in satisfying the desires of the flesh and in the glorious intoxication of song. And by his song he has sung himself into the heart of his nation and of the world at large— into the warm smell of the peasant's cottage, into the stir of his blood. His voice is the voice of his nation, for in his song his nation hears to this day its happiness, its sorrows, and all the splendour of its past. His song is in the air, and the Queen of Elfland comes stealing out of a fern in search of a soul. And out of the silence of the night come the pale ghosts of beautiful maidens long dead, who once played hide and seek with happiness:

> 'Ye flowery banks o'bonnie Doon,
> How can ye blume sae fresh and fair?
> How can ye chant, ye little birds,
> And I sae weary fu' o' care!'

But, in conclusion, let the poet speak his own sorrowful farewell:

'The fates and characters of the rhyming tribe often employ my thoughts when I am disposed to be melancholy. There is not, among all the martyrologies that ever were penned, so rueful a narrative as the lives of the poets.—In the comparative view of wretches, the criterion is not what they are doomed to suffer, but how they are formed to bear. Take a being of our kind, give him a stronger imagination and a more delicate sensibility, which between them will ever engender a more ungovernable set of passions, than the usual lot of man; implant in him an irresistible impulse to some idle vagary, such as, arranging wild flowers in fantastical nosegays, tracing the grasshopper to his haunt by his chirping song, watching the frisks of the little minnows in the sunny pool, or hunting after the intrigues of butterflies—in short, send him adrift after some pursuit which shall eternally mislead him from the paths of lucre, and yet curse him with a keener relish than any man living for the pleasures that lucre can purchase; lastly, fill up the measure of his woes by bestowing on him a spurning sense of his own dignity, and you have created a wight nearly as miserable as a poet.'

LORD BYRON (1788–1824)

Lameness and Genius

> 'My days are in the yellow leaf;
> The flowers and fruits of love are gone;
> The worm, the canker and the grief
> Are mine, alone.'

IN one of her fits of rage, Byron's mother, a quarrelsome, disillusioned, and bitter woman, once called the boy a 'lame brat'. 'I was born so, mother', Byron replied very quietly, pale with anguish. What utter pathos lies in those few words! A high-spirited lad could at best regard lameness as a cruel stroke of fate, but the suggestion that it was contemptible, contained in his mother's unforgivable outburst, made it wellnigh impossible to endure.

That Byron could never forget his infirmity all the days of his short and troubled life was his great and enduring tragedy. There were times when he suffered acutely or was filled with overwhelming ire, when hearing, or even imagining, his lameness referred to in conversation. An early instance of the sensitiveness which exposed him to wounding by every careless remark occurred when he was a very small boy. A friend talking to his nurse remarked: 'What a pretty boy Byron is, what a pity he has such a leg.' With eyes flashing, the child cut at the speaker with his toy whip, crying out 'Dinna speak of it!' A far more hurtful episode took place in 1803, when he was madly in love with a distant relative, Mary Ann Chaworth. It was the first time in his life he had really been in love, and he realized the hopelessness of his passion in a singularly cruel manner, when he accidentally overheard Mary saying to her maid: 'Do you think I could care for that lame boy?' The girl was married two years later, and in 1807 Byron sent her the lines beginning 'O had my fate

149

been join'd with thine'. He made his loss the subject of many of his verses and even so late as 1816, when he wrote the *Dream* he penned the lines amid a flood of tears.

The Nature of the Lameness

The nature of the lameness which so affected the poet's life has been the subject of much conjecture and of many wild surmises. Accounts left by his friends and contemporaries disagree as to which foot was affected. Edward John Trelawny, a brilliant but inaccurate historian, who took part in the Greek insurrection and whose curiosity caused him to draw back the covering from his friend's legs after his death, declared that both feet were affected. Byron's instrument maker said only the left leg was misshapen, while his mother said the deformity was in the right foot. This was probably correct, for James Kemble gives a description of two boots now in the possession of the publishing house of John Murray in London. Both of these fitted the right foot only. One was made when Byron was eleven years of age, the other when he was eighteen. Wedged the entire length, the single piece leather sole is raised from three-eighths to half an inch on the outside, thus indicating the *varus* element of a congenital clubfoot. After the boy had succeeded to the peerage at the age of ten, his mother engaged the services of Lavender, an ignorant and pompous Nottingham quack, who did much more harm than good by brutally attempting to twist the foot into shape and holding it in position by means of a wooden appliance. The boy gave evidence of his undoubted courage while he was subjected to the torture which this *ignoramus* inflicted. When Rogers, with whom he read Latin, was moved to cry out, 'Such pain as I know you must be suffering, my Lord!' he replied, 'Never mind, Mr Rogers, you shall not see any signs of it in me'.

Lameness curbed his ambitions, making him shy and timid; and as he attempted to follow ambition and to overcome—or was it to disguise?—his feelings of inferiority arising from the deformity, he waxed aggressive, arrogant, defiant. These compensatory characteristics were in evidence in his dealings with his fellows, and more than anything else, influenced his writing. He was a man of contradictions. Friends and servants were devoted to him because he could be genial and considerate, but because he was apt to be overbearing the number of his friendships was limited. To rivals he was often ungenerous, and like his hero Pope, he was vindictive toward those who attacked him.

When his great-uncle died in 1798, Byron, at the age of ten, succeeded to the title and estates, becoming George Gordon, sixth Lord Byron. Up to the age of thirteen, when he was entered at Harrow, his schooling had been unsatisfactory, due largely to his mother's interference. The Headmaster, Dr Joseph Drury, a man of great discernment, saw that in Byron he had to deal with 'a wild mountain-colt', and realized that he was 'to be led by a silken string rather than by a cable'. Throughout the poet's career we find evidence that this judgement was substantially correct. No one was more responsive to kindness and to the gentle approach, none more wilful and mulish when opposed, when thwarted, or confronted with tactlessness.

The thought of being humbled and degraded at school caused the boy acute agony of mind. Many junior to him were more advanced in learning, and Drury displayed much wisdom in telling him that he would not be 'placed' until he was on more equal terms with boys of his own age.

The Gift for Satire

Scarcely had Byron started on his literary career than he was called upon to display his gift for satire. Following the notoriously, and quite unnecessarily, savage review of *Hours of Idleness* in the *Edinburgh Review*, he bided his time for launching his devastating reply, *English Bards and Scotch Reviewers*. This was an enlargement and an elaboration of a satire which he had written in 1807 and which he had called *British Bards*. The young man well understood that the success or failure of the reply would have a profound influence upon his future career. He strove, therefore, to make the satire even more vitriolic and to give the work all the brilliance he could command. When it appeared, three days after the noble author had taken his seat in the House of Lords, its reception left him in no doubt that he had exacted a full, if brutal, revenge.

In many ways Byron was childishly simple. Commenting on the first two cantos of *Childe Harold*, he said they contained the experience of one at least ten years older than his age when they were written. He could not believe that he could be outdone, and his vanity was for ever reflected in the recapitulation of real or imagined experiences and sufferings. In the notes to the second canto of *Childe Harold* he drew a comparison between an Albanian servant who had wept on leaving him, and Lord De La Warr, who had excused himself from visiting Byron on the grounds that he had a prior engagement. This incident had occurred on the day before Byron left London on his Albanian tour. To De La Warr and to most of its readers, this passage must have seemed petty, but to the self-conscious poet his friend's action seemed like the basest desertion.

He was persistent in his attacks on 'cant political, religious, and moral', and this was one of the chief reasons for the popularity of his works. His verse appealed by reason of its wit and fluency, and because it was readily understandable. In depicting the Oriental scenes in which so many of his characters moved, he captured the imagination of his readers who were made to share the enthusiasm for the East which had stirred the poet from early boyhood. Apart from historical works, accounts of travels in the East were his greatest delight—'All books upon the East I could meet with I had read before I was ten years old.' The lameness which prevented him from taking a full part in the outdoor pursuits of his fellow scholars had helped to form his taste for reading and to amass a bizarre assortment of knowledge.

Following the instantaneous and unprecedented success of the first cantos of *Childe Harold* Byron had the world at his feet. Small wonder if so much flattery spoilt him utterly! And as the centre of attraction in the world of literature and society he found it fatally easy to win the favours of the opposite sex—a peer of England, who had dedicated his life to the Muses; devastatingly handsome with joyous, shining eyes, sensitive capricious mouth, Grecian profile, pale delicate face; charming, generous, and—rich.

Byron could be cruel, and in his criticisms of the young Keats he displayed a lamentable lack of decency and much of that pettiness which tended to mar his work. Writing to Murray he referred to the 'trash' that the publisher had sent him. The volume in question contained the Odes *To a Nightingale*, *On a Grecian Urn*, and *Hyperion*! He went on to speak of the brother poet's 'drivelling idiotism'. In a later letter he said: 'The *Edinburgh* praises Jack Keats or Ketch, or whatever his names are.' Within a few months Keats was dead, and Byron, whose only real quarrel with him had rested on his criticism of Pope, began to feel ashamed of his venomous attacks.

Byron's place in English poetry has shifted with the varying tastes of different ages. In his lifetime there was an upsurge of dissatisfaction with the existing order, and his satirical powers won the approbation of those who welcomed one who could attack the persons and institutions of which they disapproved. He was generally acknowledged as the foremost poet of his day, but in 1860 a reviewer found this judgement a subject for mirth. Carlyle counselled his readers to read Goethe, while opining that Byron had now (1839) 'reached a very low level'. Goethe, however, had the greatest admiration for Byron's work and urged Eckermann to learn English in order that he might appreciate it in the original. Time has brought Byron again to the fore, and the Continental writers in particular are almost unanimous in assigning to him the place of honour among the poets of his age.

Escape from the Ill Humours

Byron's work is marred by many imperfections. He wrote with extreme rapidity and with very little care, so that minute dissection of his lines shows traces of slovenliness. 'I am like the tiger,' he said, 'if I miss the first spring, I go grumbling back to my jungle.' When he took his revenge on the *Edinburgh* reviewer, he learned that the public had a taste for malice salted with wit, and in later works he both shocked and amused his contemporaries by his scathing satires. This kind of writing was also a means of ridding himself of the ill humours which arose from the consciousness of his infirmity.

His early successes brought him the adulation which he affected to despise but which in reality was very dear to his heart. Even when he was the most talked-of man in England, he was never free from the torments which brooding on his lameness had engendered. He was vain of his exceptional good looks. On one occasion his friend Scrope Davies entered the poet's bedroom while he still slept, and was astonished to see that the beautiful and much admired hair was in curl-papers. Byron was angry at being thus discovered but, accepting the situation, declared 'I'm a d——d fool'. His friend said he had thought the hair curled naturally, to which Byron replied, 'Yes, naturally, every night; but don't let the cat out of the bag, for I'm as vain of my curls as a girl of sixteen'. In one to whom appearance meant so much, lameness must have been a dire tragedy. On entering a room he would attempt to hide it by running rather than walking, stopping himself by planting the sound foot on the ground and resting on it. He rarely walked in the streets, but when he did so he moved with a sliding gait on the balls and toes of his feet. One day he was walking with his great friend, Hobhouse, when he stopped and accused him, 'Now I know you're looking at my foot'. In all other respects he was of remarkable personal beauty, and there is no doubt that in his mind this single blemish was magnified out of all proportion. His writing was influenced in two ways. In his satirical works he frequently went out of his way to be unkind and seems to have found in an ungenerous stroke of the satirical pen the same sort of satisfaction which some deformed people find in inflicting physical pain. And, secondly, much of his fine lyrical poetry is tinged with melancholy and a wistfulness such as we find in *Lara:*

> 'There was in him a vital scorn of all:
> As if the worst had fallen which could befall,
> He stood a stranger in this breathing world,
> An erring Spirit from another hurled;
> A thing of dark imaginings. . . .
>
> With more capacity for love than Earth
> Bestows on most of mortal mould and birth,
> His early dreams of good outstripped the truth,
> And troubled Manhood followed baffled Youth. . . .'

In his fine study of Byron, *The Pilgrim of Eternity*, John Drinkwater points out that the poet's detractors were often so obsessed by his defects that they were blinded to his merits. He goes on to mention the 'daring, the tenderness, the candour and the fortitude' that went to the making of a nature which was essentially heroic.

In 1816 Byron left England for the last time. He had become a social exile. Following the separation from his wife he was accused of all manner of vice and was exposed to public insult. When he went to Italy the failure of his marriage does not seem to have left him in the depths of despair, nor a prey to melancholy. At twenty-eight he had tasted the sweetness and the bitterness of life, and with no particular ambition to fulfil he proceeded on his way in a mood of comparative calm. From now on his life, apart from the Greek episode at its end, was without definite purpose. He wandered, philandered, entertained a few visitors from home, and all the rest was poetry—imperishable poetry which raised him to the stature of greatness.

Byron's output during his remaining years was amazing by any standards, but when one considers how much of his best work falls within that period it becomes all the more remarkable. In *The Prisoner of Chillon* he displayed his lyrical powers to great advantage, and after reading it, none, surely, could maintain that he lacked tenderness and feeling. His mood when writing the fourth canto of *Childe Harold* may be judged from the following lines:

> 'We wither from our youth, we gasp away—
> Sick—sick; unfound the boon, unslaked the thirst,
> Though to the last, in verge of our decay,
> Some phantom lures, such as we thought at first—
> But all too late,—so are we doubly curst.
> Love, Fame, Ambition, Avarice—'tis the same,
> Each idle—and all ill—and none the worst—
> For all are meteors with a different name,
> And Death the sable smoke where vanishes the flame.'

On My Thirty-Third Birthday, the lines with which the poet celebrated the anniversary in 1821, are, for all their wry humour, a sad commentary:

> 'Through life's dull road, so dim and dirty,
> I have dragg'd to three-and-thirty.
> What have these years left to me?
> Nothing—except thirty-three.'

Work—an Anodyne

To understand the tragedy of those years of exile one has only to remember how often Byron said that he looked upon work only as an escape from life—an anodyne. 'I have not the least idea where I am going, nor what I am to do.' It would be idle to pretend that he was careless of the reception accorded his poetry in later years, but these

LORD BYRON
(1788–1824)

defiant lines from a letter to Murray show a fine independence:

'I know the precise worth of popular applause, for few scribblers
have had more of it; and if I chose to swerve into their paths, I could
retain it, or resume it. But I neither love ye, nor fear ye; and though
I buy with ye and sell with ye, and talk with ye, I will neither eat
with ye, nor pray with ye. They made me, without my search, a
species of popular idol—they, without reason or judgment, beyond
the caprice of their good pleasure, threw down the image from its
pedestal; it was not broken with the fall, and they would, it seems,
again replace it,—but they shall not.'

In 1822, probably between April and July, Byron wrote
his drama, *The Deformed Transformed*. The opening
scene was clearly derived from the childhood incident
when his mother's hasty words caused him so much
anguish.

> Bertha: Out, hunchback!
> Arnold: I was born so, mother!

It is interesting to note that Mary Shelley, in her copy of
the work, wrote: 'No action of Lord Byron's life—scarce
a line he has written—but was influenced by his personal
defect.' This probably is putting the case too highly, but
the writer's opinion must command respect.

The following extract from Clare Clairmont's diary
shows that she possessed unusual critical acumen for a
girl aged twenty-three, but it displays also the bias which
their relationship made practically inevitable. William
Godwin's step-daughter had given herself to Byron,
though he never pretended to love her and certainly never
pursued her. Her remarks, then, must be treated with the
caution required when examining the statements of 'a
woman scorned':

'His song is woven of the commonest and grossest elements of our
nature: desire, hatred, revenge, a proneness to mischief, spoliation and
cruelty. . . . His appeals to freedom . . .' were rendered null and
void, declared Clare, by 'a marked animosity to philosophy and
virtue.'

This assessment is, of course, too superficial to explain so much that is fine in Byron's poetry. In November, 1821, when he was on the road between Florence and Pisa, he wrote these stanzas:

'Oh, talk not to me of a name great in story;
The days of our youth are the days of our glory;
And the myrtle and ivy of sweet two-and-twenty
Are worth all your laurels, though ever so plenty.

What are garlands and crowns to the brow that is wrinkled?
'Tis but as a dead-flower with May-dew besprinkled.
Then away with all such from the head that is hoary!
What care I for the wreaths that can *only* give glory !

Oh Fame!—If I e'er took delight in thy praises,
'Twas less for the sake of thy high-sounding phrases,
Than to see the bright eyes of the dear one discover,
She thought that I was not unworthy to love her.

There chiefly I sought thee, *there* only I found thee;
Her glance was the best of the rays that surround thee;
When it sparkled o'er aught that was bright in my story,
I knew it was love, and I felt it was glory.'

Had Byron not been cursed with the lameness which Macaulay called 'the bad fairy's bundle', the object of what was probably his only real love, Mary Anne Chaworth, might have thought him 'not unworthy to love her'. Able to take part in the dance which he affected to despise, and able to participate in those activities which were denied him, Byron's poetry might well have followed a different pattern.

A Greek Tragedy

To the sympathetic reader the tale of Byron's life reads

like a Greek tragedy which, its end being already familiar, is so painfully slow in unfolding itself.

In 1821 Greece rose in arms against the Turks. The cry of liberty echoed through the length and breadth of Hellas. In May, 1823, Byron who from childhood had loved

'the isles of Greece, the isles of Greece!
Where burning Sappho loved and sung,
Where grew the arts of war and peace,
Where Delos rose, and Phoebus sprung!'

decided to join the Greek insurgents, landing at Missolonghi in the following January.

'The mountains look on Marathon—
And Marathon looks on the sea;
And musing there an hour alone,
I dream't that Greece might still be free.'

Three months after his arrival he was caught in a rainstorm, catching a chill from which he never recovered. The exact cause of his death remains shrouded in mystery. Was it uraemia, marsh fever, typhoid, rheumatic fever, to which he succumbed? Towards the evening of April 19 a terrible storm was raging. Thunder and lightning rent the sky as the troubled soul of George Gordon Noel Byron, Right Honourable and Wicked Peer of the Realm of England, passed into eternity. And in the darkness of the night the Greek peasants cried 'Byron is dead!' and 'Byron is dead!' tolled like a funeral bell through the land that gave him birth. Byron's mortal body was taken back to England and buried in the village church at Hucknall Torkard.

''Tis time this heart should be unmoved,
Since others it hath ceased to move:
Yet, though I cannot be beloved,
Still let me love!

My days are in the yellow leaf;
The flowers and fruits of love are gone;
The worm, the canker, and the grief,
Are mine alone!

The fire that on my bosom preys
Is lone as some volcanic isle;
No torch is kindled at its blaze—
A funeral pile.'

ALEXANDER POPE (1688–1744)

Physical Infirmity and Genius

'Good nature and good sense must ever join;
To err is human, to forgive divine.'

WITH the exception of Shakespeare, Alexander Pope
in the land that gave him birth is the most quoted of
all poets. The couplet prefacing this chapter may serve
as an appropriate text as we consider the career and work
of its author. In the life of Pope there is much to admire,
to deplore, and to regret. His place in English literature
is unique, even though some critics have denied his right
to be considered a great poet, on the grounds that he
lacked the true poetic fire. Yet his gift for enshrining in
memorable verse the innermost thoughts to which ordinary men are unable to give adequate expression has been
surpassed only by Shakespeare. Men and women who
know nothing about the author quote, or misquote, in
their every-day speech those familiar lines which have
assumed a place of pride and intimacy in the English
language: 'Hope springs eternal in the human breast';
'Fools rush in where angels fear to tread'; 'A little learning
is a dang'rous thing.'

Alexander Pope was born on May 21, 1688—a year of
ill-omen for a child of Roman Catholic parentage. His
father, a successful linen draper, soon retired from
business to live at Binfield, a sleepy village on the borders
of Windsor Forest. The year which witnessed the flight
of James II saw the frustration of Roman Catholic hopes,
for the intolerance of the age debarred them from the law,
the church, and politics. Alexander's indulgent parents,
both of whom were forty-six years of age when their puny
child was born, had the means to afford him sufficient
compensation for the disadvantage of belonging to an
ostracized sect. But for this, his start in life would indeed

have been unenviable. Destined though he was to become a satirist whose shafts of malicious wit pierced the heaviest armour of his adversaries, his life was one 'long disease'.

Deformed, sickly, and frail from birth, Pope's early education was received at home. After spending a short time at a school in Twyford, he returned to Binfield, to resume his desultory private studies. He suffered severely from headaches—an affliction which clouded his whole life and undermined his manliness. This handicap he inherited from his mother, while his father passed on to him a tendency to curvature of the spine. Acquiring a vast and remarkable knowledge of English literature and a passion for poetry, he overtaxed himself at puberty by too much studying and suffered a nervous breakdown. The headaches now gave him little respite, and his restless mind sank into strange fits of lethargy. By good fortune the patient was seen by Dr. John Radcliffe, one of the most successful practitioners of his day, who placed him on a diet, restricted his work, and prescribed daily rides in Windsor Forest. This sensible treatment quickly produced a complete recovery.

In 1704 Pope, who had fallen under the influence of Dryden, wrote the *Pastorals*. He was then only sixteen years of age, but another five years had to elapse before these were published in Tonson's *Poetic Miscellanies*, 1709. In that year he penned his first important work, the immortal *Essay on Criticism*, which, published in 1711, gave the first indication of his genius for packing thought and uncanny aptness of word within a single line or couplet.

The Youthful Lover

To a Young Lady with a Volume of Voiture (1712) owed much to his intimacy with two daughters of a Roman Catholic family living in a fine old Elizabethan mansion, Mapledurham, within a few miles of Binfield. The poet was nineteen years old when he first met Teresa and Martha Blount, and he soon lost his impressionable heart to Teresa, the elder and more beautiful of the sisters. It was not long, however, before he began to declare his devotion to both—alternately or together. This dual attraction gave way in turn to a steadfast and enduring regard for Martha ('Blue-eyed Patty Blount') who was seventeen, fair-haired, and warm of heart. At the same time his feelings towards Teresa changed to apathy. His relations with Martha were in the nature of an innocent friendship, though his letters to her contained mention of things which may be explained by the coarseness of the age, but which illustrate his utter lack of chivalry and decency. But for his bodily infirmities, Martha might well have become the invalid's wife, though she could scarcely have been more than a nurse to him, for marriage in the accepted sense would have been a mockery. As ill-health brought him to a premature old age, Pope continued to regard Martha with the rosy eyes of the youthful lover as a radiantly beautiful girl. The soft white skin which once had charmed his heart was now cruelly scarred by the ravages of smallpox; only the fine blue eyes retained the loveliness of youth. When the poet died he left the woman he had loved all his life almost his entire fortune.

In 1714 Pope was amongst those who frequented the literary club in which Addison had installed his man Daniel Button. Incensed by a series of papers which Thomas Tickell contributed to the *Guardian*, praising Ambrose Philips and neglecting his own work, Pope revenged himself wittily by means of a subterfuge which was characteristic of his Machiavellian willingness to sacrifice scruples to expediency. He sent a paper purporting to be a continuation of the series to the *Guardian*, and, comparing the *Pastorals* of Philips with his own, bestowed ironical praise on all that he considered worst in his rival's work, while condemning both himself and Virgil. It is said that Steele showed Pope the contribution, which he did not wish to publish. Pope pretended to be unconcerned and counselled that it should appear. It was printed and afforded those who understood the situation much amusement; Philips, however, was furious at the trick played upon him. He is said to have hung up a birch-rod in Button's, vowing that he would use it on the person of his tormentor whenever he appeared. Whether for this or some other reason, Pope discontinued his visits to the Club.

The Wicked Wasp of Twickenham

The story of Pope's friendship and ultimate quarrel with Lady Mary Wortley Montagu throws a flood of light on his character. Their first meeting seems to have taken place in 1715, when the poet was basking in the homage accorded by society to the author of the *Essay on Criticism*, *The Rape of the Lock*, and the translation of Homer. Lady Mary, besides possessing all the attributes of birth and breeding, was acknowledged to be the wittiest woman in England. She was also dazzlingly beautiful, and Pope, whose romantic disposition caused him to dwell much on imagined love, was flattered by her attention, convinced that he occupied a special corner in her life. His letters to her are lavish with saccharine compliments: 'I had ten times rather go on pilgrimage to see your face, than St. John Baptist's head.' Lady Mary was amused at his extravagances, and her replies reflect both her good breeding and her quiet humour. While Pope was an incurable romantic, her head was never ruled by her heart. When they became neighbours at Twickenham, her wit and his flights of fancy proved less amusing at close quarters than when distance lent enchantment.

According to Lady Mary Wortley Montagu the cause of the quarrel which ended their friendship was 'that at some ill-chosen time, when she least expected what romances call a declaration, he made such passionate love to her as, in spite of her utmost endeavours to be angry and look grave, provoked an immoderate fit of laughter, from which moment he became her implacable enemy'. Thus, without in the least meaning to do so, she had inflicted on him the worst possible injury by acting as though he were an object of ridicule. Pope swore bitter revenge. Out for her blood, he introduced this couplet in the *Dunciad*:

'Whence hapless Monsieur much complains at Paris
Of wrongs from Duchesses and Lady Maries.'

Feeling, perhaps, that this was too obscure, he added a note to the 1729 edition: 'This passage was thought to allude to a famous lady who cheated a French wit of £5,000 in the South Sea year. But the author meant it in general of all bragging travellers, and of all w—— and cheats under the name of ladies.' This note was a reference to the fact that Lady Mary received from a Monsieur Rémond, whom she met on her way home from Constantinople, a sum of money to invest on his behalf. In 1720 he visited Twickenham, when she advised him to sell some South Sea Stock and leave her to reinvest the proceeds. Unfortunately, the sum was reinvested in the South Sea, and shortly afterwards the Stock fell more than half. On hearing of this catastrophe, the Frenchman pretended to disbelieve her and threatened to publish certain of her letters if he were not repaid. Apparently the lady managed to placate him, for the matter was not made public.

Subsequently Pope and Lady Mary engaged in a brisk exchange of insults which appeared in various publications. Her attacks were as personal and as malicious as his, but not so vulgar, for Pope's couplets even exposed to the public gaze the intimacies of her toilet and contained allusions to her dirty underlinen. When the proud lady's married life ended in disaster, the poet's underhanded manoeuvres had done irreparable harm to her social career. After separating from her husband she left her native land, to become a legend before her time. Like many others, she had found out that it did not pay to stir up the little man whom she had dubbed the 'wicked wasp of Twickenham'.

Pope had discovered at an early date that his success in

life depended upon his ability to please the public taste with his writings, for his religion made any question of winning political advancement impossible. Despite his superficial knowledge of Greek, his verse translation of Homer brought him financial recompense unprecedented in the annals of English literature, and phenomenal and growing fame, and gave him access to the most exclusive social circles. It was natural that the rise of this trades-man's son excited the envy of certain less fortunate writers, with some of whom Pope became involved in acrimonious clashes. Nothing shows his love of subter-ranean methods more than the manner in which he launched the *Dunciad*. In its first form this may have been written as early as 1720, and it is certain that a version was completed in 1725. The poem first appeared, however, in 1728, by which time the author had drawn the fire of his enemies by a skilfully baited trap. He wished his satire to be considered as a defensive weapon, and to this end he published *Bathos*, one chapter of which contained so many personalities that 'for half a year or more the common newspapers were filled with the most abusive falsehoods and scurrilities they could possibly devise'.

Pope now had his justification for publishing, and soon the town was gloating over this wholesale slaughter of the innocents. The addition of new victims to each suc-ceeding edition of the *Dunciad* up to the time of Pope's death showed that the work was not designed, as he declared, 'to drag into light the common enemies of mankind', but to chastise all who had done him personal injury. Although the majority of those castigated in its pages were obscure scribblers whose works have long since been forgotten, their names have survived the passing of more than two centuries. For this they have to thank the poem which is still read for the brilliant satire in which they were made to suffer for their temerity in criticizing its author.

Pope, whose life had been one continuous round of physical suffering, died of 'asthmatical dropsy'. At the suggestion of his friend, the first Viscount Bolingbroke,

the notorious quack Joshua ('Spot') Ward was called in
to prescribe for the patient, who seems to have been as
inordinately fond of quacks as he was of changing his
doctor, sometimes having three or four at a time. Ward,
whose success as a quack brought him a fortune, is
mentioned in several of Pope's satires:

> 'Of late, without the least pretence to skill,
> Ward's grown a famed physician by a pill.'

This second line refers to the quack's 'universal remedy'—
a highly dangerous compound of antimony.

The asthma failed to respond to any treatment, and in
April, 1744, another notorious quack, Thompson, was
consulted, who drew off 'a great quantity of pure water'
and pretended to see signs of improvement in the patient's
condition. Pope, however, knew differently, and when a
friend called on him declared: 'Here am I dying from a
hundred good symptoms.' He faced death with equan-
imity and shortly before the end said: 'I am so certain
of the soul's being immortal, that I feel it within me as it
were by intuition.' He died peacefully, almost imperceptibly, on May 30, 744, at the age of fifty-six.

Alexander the Little

Sir Joshua Reynolds described Pope as 'about four feet
six high, very hump-backed and deformed. He had a very
large and very fine eye.' His constant headaches left their
mark in the form of a permanent contraction of the skin
above the eyebrows. He was accustomed to having his
pathetically thin legs swathed in three pairs of stockings,
both to increase their bulk and as a protection against cold
to which he was morbidly sensitive. A maid had to draw
the stockings on and off for him, for he was too weak to
dress or undress himself unaided. In his efforts to keep
warm, he wore a fur doublet under a shirt of coarse warm
linen. On rising, he was encased in a bodice of stiff
canvas, and without this support he was scarcely able to
stand erect. His chair had to be raised to bring him to the

level of the table. In a letter to John Caryll, the Roman Catholic Sussex squire, he gives this glimpse of the disabilities which make his industry all the more remarkable:

'I have lain under an impediment to all amusement and pleasure these months, namely, very great indispositions, and such an alteration in my constitution, as rather deserves to be called a ruin than a revolution. I have had no appetite or digestion a vast while. I have perpetual vomitings and nervous distempers upon me, with a dejection of spirits that has totally taken away everything, if I ever had anything, which could be called vivacity or cheerfulness.'

In a letter to Martha Blount he describes a bizarre remedy:

'As to my health I am in a very odd course for the pain in my side; I mean a course of brickbats and tiles, which they apply to me piping hot, morning and night; and sure it is very satisfactory to one who loves architecture at his heart to be built round in his very bed. My body may properly at this time be called a human structure.'

Within this pathetic mortal frame dwelt a complex, alert, and powerful mind, acutely sensitive to beauty, yearning for romance, pathologically vain, tormented by the ridicule excited by the physical shortcomings of the body. In consequence he was often driven to adopt most unworthy means to take vengeance for any slight, real or imagined, and at times he stooped to downright dishonesty. Terrible or ludicrous in his wrath, he yet was capable of real kindness of heart and gentleness of spirit to those in distress. Lord Chesterfield wrote that 'Pope was as great an instance as any he quotes of the contrarieties and inconsistencies of human nature; for notwithstanding the malignancy of his satires and some blamable passages of his life, he was charitable to his power, active to do good offices, and piously attentive to an old bed-ridden mother who died but a little time before him.' In addition to his constant headaches, Pope's chief complaint was indigestion. The former he thought he could relieve by drinking large quantities of coffee, but the latter he made worse by indulging in his favourite dish, potted lampreys, and in liqueurs.

Pope's upbringing played an important rôle in the

formation of his character. Instead of experiencing the give and take which is part and parcel of school-life, he was cut off from the society of boys of his own age, and devoting himself almost exclusively to reading and writing, he may be said to have had no childhood. Living at home with indulgent parents, he had more of his own way than was good for him, and knew no opposition until he embarked on his literary career. His early efforts at versification were eulogized, and he was regarded as a prodigy. In later years his vanity and insincerity caused him to change the dates of certain of his writings in order to give the appearance of even greater precocity.

As an instance of his vulnerability where criticism was concerned the following incident may be quoted. Shortly after the *Essay on Man* had been published anonymously, he asked his friend, David Mallet, the poet, if there was anything new in literature. The reply: 'Nothing worth notice; only a thing called an "Essay on Man", made up of shocking poetry and insufferable philosophy,' threw the author into such a rage that he foamed at the mouth and screamed 'I wrote it!' whereupon his abashed friend hurriedly fled. Over the value of this *Essay* as a contribution to philosophy, there has been much controversy, some bestowing on it the most lavish praise and others regarding it as dreary and worthless. Whatever its merits and demerits, it affords a striking example of Pope's genius for crystallizing the thoughts of the common man in language which gives them beauty and perpetuity and raises them to the stature of epigrams. The following extract well exemplifies this gift:

> 'God loves from Whole to Parts: but human soul
> Must rise from Individual to the Whole.
> Self-love but serves the virtuous mind to wake,
> As the small pebble stirs the peaceful lake;
> The centre mov'd, a circle straight succeeds,
> Another still, and still another spreads;
> Friend, parent, neighbour, first it will embrace;
> His country next; and next all human race;
> Wide and more wide, th' o'erflowings of the mind
> Take ev'ry creature in, of ev'ry kind;

Earth smiles around, with boundless beauty blest,
And Heav'n beholds its image in his breast.'

The Rape of the Lock, the most delicious and beautifully contrived example of its kind, shows the versatility of one who could also display the deep understanding of human nature evident in *Eloisa to Abelard:*

'Assist me, heav'n! but whence arose that pray'r
Sprung it from piety or from despair?
Ev'n here, where frozen chastity retires,
Love finds an altar for forbidden fires.
I ought to grieve, but cannot what I ought;
I mourn the lover, not lament the fault;
I view my crime, but kindle at the view,
Repent old pleasures, and solicit new;
Now turn'd to heav'n, I weep my past offence,
Now think of thee, and curse my innocence.
Of all affliction taught a lover yet,
'Tis sure the hardest science to forget!'

'That Long Disease, his Life'

In the autobiographical *Epistle to Dr. Arbuthnot* Pope referred to 'that long disease, his life'. Remembering this, we can but marvel at the prominent part he played in freeing poetry from the artificiality introduced by seventeenth-century writers. Posthumous glory had been the ambition of this little man who longed to subsist in the memory and the wonder of generations yet unborn. Paradoxically, the incongruence of time has brought virtual oblivion on the man, yet his words are still on the lips of posterity. His greatest tragedy was that he failed to school himself to bear without bitterness the burden of sickness and misfortune, to rise triumphant over the tribulations of the flesh. Thus he was never destined to attain full spiritual stature. His only weapon was wit, sharpened on the whetstone of malice. Sometimes he used it to inflict mortal wounds, sometimes merely to prick the bubbles of vanity and folly. For its misuse we must blame his physical infirmities; for the superlative skill with which he directed his thrusts we must pay tribute to the genius imprisoned in a pathetic frame.

LAFCADIO HEARN (1850–1904)

Disfigured Genius Who Worshipped Beauty

> 'I do indeed revere Woman as the
> Creator, and I respect—yes, I almost
> believe in — the graceful Hellenic
> anthropomorphism which worshipped
> feminine softness and serpentine fascin-
> ation and intoxicating loveliness in the
> garb of Venus Anadyomene.'

BORN on an island that once upon a time was the abode of Sappho, Lafcadio Hearn all his life wrote the most polished, beautiful, and lyrical prose. His was a veritable genius for choosing harmonious and haunting words. Fastidious disciple of Flaubert, Gautier, de Maupassant, he would go to the most extreme lengths in his efforts to convey exquisite niceties of meaning. It is said that on one occasion he worked for eight months polishing and repolishing seventy-three lines. This almost pathological seeking after consummate perfection of style, however, was not matched by breadth of vision and sympathetic insight into the frailties of human nature, which are the essential requisites for those who desire to impress themselves lastingly on the minds of men. Excelling almost all modern writers in point of style, Lafcadio Hearn failed to win immortality. What manner of man was he? What were the forces which directed his strangely warped, beauty-famished soul?

How Shall a Man Escape from his Ancestors?

Charles Bush Hearn, a surgeon-major in the British army, came of a Dorsetshire family in which English, Irish, and a tinge of gipsy blood were intermingled. In the course of duty he went to the Grecian island of Santa

Maura in the Aegean, the ancient Leucadia, where 'burning Sappho' had loved and sung. Here he met and married Rosa Tessima, a devastatingly beautiful Greek girl in whom there was a strain of Arab and Moorish blood. Patricio Lafcadio Tessima Carlos Hearn was born on June 27, 1850; Lafcadio, the name by which he was to become known, was taken from Leucadia. A crowd of conflicting instincts all his days of vanity were to war within him: Anglo-Saxon repression, Oriental sensuousness, Arab apathy, gipsy restlessness. He was only two years old when his father was ordered to the West Indies, leaving wife and child in care of relatives at Dublin.

The mother, hot tempered and impetuous, soon found her environment unutterably prosaic and intolerable, and leaving the seven-year-old boy to the none-too-tender care of her husband's aunt, fled into the Unknown. Lafcadio spent a lonely and joyless childhood. In 1863 he was sent to St Cuthbert's College, Ushaw, Durham, where he was to study for the priesthood. Here, at the age of sixteen, tragedy overtook him, and its shadow clouded his life, pursuing him to the gates of the tomb. Taking part in the game 'Giant's Stride', he was struck in the face by the wooden handle at the end of a rope which flew back. The blow damaged his left eye severely, and lack of skilled attention was followed by inflammation and subsequent total blindness, the cornea becoming permanently coated with a milky film.

His addiction to reading meant that the sound eye was now subjected to excessive strain, and in time it became swollen to twice the normal size, and protruding, while vision was seriously affected. This blemish had the most disastrous effect upon Hearn, who developed an inferiority complex, imagining himself to be physically repulsive. He was particularly sensitive about the defect when in the company of women, and his relations with them were governed by this hopeless feeling of inferiority. In time he acquired the habit of placing one hand over his eye when talking with anyone, and in later years he tended to shut himself off from the world of man and to live in the world of books.

One day the young Lafcadio shocked the Jesuit fathers by proudly announcing that he had turned pantheist. In disgrace he was transferred to another Jesuit school, the 'Petits Précepteurs' near Rouen in France. Once again his rebellious spirit got him into trouble, and running away from school he made his way to the Latin Quarter of Paris, and in 1869, as it were casually, drifted to New York.

Arrived in the great metropolis, his prospects were of the blackest. Shy, half blind, without a single friend to whom he could turn for help or advice, unequipped to make any headway in this new and strange environment, he just managed to exist by performing the most menial tasks, which included waiting in a cheap restaurant. Making his way to Cincinnati, he went through a similar dreary round of transitory employments, half starved and frequently having nowhere to sleep but a hayloft or a rusty boiler on a rubbish dump. He lasted one day as a messenger boy, for another he peddled the wares of a Syrian itinerant vendor of mirrors. Having been given a post in the public library, his love of books was his undoing; he was discharged because he read so much that he neglected his duties.

Then fortune smiled on him for a while. A goodhearted old English printer, Henry Watkin, took an interest in him, allowed him to sleep in his shop, taught him to set type, and helped him to obtain a job with a paper called the *Trade List*. In 1873 Hearn gave up this work to write feature articles for the *Cincinnati Enquirer*. His contributions were remarkable for their pure English, and he succeeded in writing beautifully of things ugly and gruesome. Visiting unsavoury places, he became more and more intrigued by the macabre and by the fascination and horror of evil. In 1874, when he reported the revolting 'Tan Yard Case', in which the murderer had attempted to burn the remains of his victim, his handling of the gruesome theme created a literary sensation.

One of Hearn's inheritances from his Greek mother was a passion for beauty, and in his writings he leaned toward the French school, with Flaubert, Gautier, and Baudelaire as his particular favourites. The sensuality in the stories and poems of these masters, the craftsmanship which demanded that every paragraph, every sentence, every line, should be more perfect than perfection, had an irresistible appeal for him. Steeping himself in works whose construction was so much in accord with his worship of beauty of form, he painstakingly translated Gautier's *Avatar*. He knew that the prejudices of the age made its publication impossible, and so the work was destroyed, but he had not laboured in vain, for the experience helped considerably in moulding his own style.

Enchantress of Ebony Thigh

Lafcadio Hearn's physical disability with its consequent feeling of inferiority prevented him from cultivating the society of women of his own class. For this reason, and also because he was poor, he became entangled with a mulatto woman, Althea Foley, with whom he lived openly. It is tempting to wonder if his master Baudelaire's lascivious eulogy of his 'enchantress of ebony thigh, born of dark midnights, the elixir of thy lips, where love flaunts his Pavan, do I crave more than steadfast affection, opium's dreams, or night's darkling shade' may have inspired the liaison. In the alchemy of Hearn's carnal lust there may have been, also, an element of atavism. Closing his eyes against the cold, practical, progressive, unlovely world of reality that was America, and against the hopeless emptiness of to-morrow, his imagination may have wandered back to the days when he was a Moorish lord and the immensity of his desires was inflamed by the voluptuous black nakedness of his Nubian concubines. The Ohio law forbade miscegenation, and Hearn's application for a marriage licence was refused. The scandal arising from the affair caused his dismissal from the *Enquirer*, but he was not thrown out of employment, for the *Cincinnati Commercial* was quick to enlist his services.

In 1877 Lafcadio and Althea parted company. The strain of overwork had left him broken in health, and treated by many as a social outcast he left Cincinnati and went to New Orleans. After his death in Japan, Althea, claiming to be his lawful wedded wife and now his widow, sought unsuccessfully to establish her right to the 'fortune' which she supposed him to have left.

Hearn arrived in the semi-tropical city of New Orleans with the *Commercial's* commission to contribute a series of articles on political conditions in Louisiana, but his beautifully written descriptions were devoid of any reference to politics, a fact which lost him his job. For many months he sought work, but his physical appearance was against him. Only five feet three inches in height, he was clad in an oversize pea-jacket, and with a very low collar and a black string tie which was much too big, he resembled 'a miniature but serious-minded scarecrow'. He had a clear olive skin and the face of a weasel. The broad, high forehead was concealed by the cap which, resembling that of a railway conductor, was affected by its wearer because the peak cast a shadow over his protruding eye. His nose was prominent and hooked, with nostrils that quivered when he was excited. The sensitive mouth was partially covered by a drooping moustache; the chin was weak. That he was conscious of the shape of his nose is clear from several of his letters. 'You remember the form of my nose?' he wrote in 1884. 'It is already become altered: it is lengthening—orientalizing. Some awful anthropologic and ethnologic change must be taking place within me!' He had small and beautifully shaped hands, and he walked with soft, stealthy, almost feline steps. On his arrival in New Orleans he wore thick spectacles which he later pawned.

Hearn's difficulty in finding a job was due largely to an epidemic of yellow fever which ravaged the city. Vividly he comments on the stillness of the streets, the torpor of the wharfs, the army of men pouring carbolic acid down the gutters; on the bizarre and often pathetic new 'cures' for the dread malady, advertised almost daily. He himself escaped yellow fever, though he contracted dengue or the break-bone fever, which left him exhausted and further weakened the sight of his remaining eye. After seven months he began to work for the *Item*, his varied experiences providing him with material for editorials exposing the evils of child labour, police extortion, and lynching. He also wrote book-reviews, charming translations from contemporary French writers, and a series of short stories. All the while he laboured untiringly to reach perfection in style.

Just as he was never happy for long in the company of one woman, he was never happy for long in one place, and having a fancy to visit the West Indies, he started a five-cent restaurant, the 'Hard Times', to raise money for the trip. Unfortunately his partner turned out to be a rogue, decamping with both the cash and the cook, and Hearn lost his entire savings.

In 1882 Lafcadio Hearn published his first book to bear his name on the title-page—*One of Cleopatra's Nights*— an exquisite rendering of six stories by Gautier. He gradually became known further afield, and his work was accepted by the *Century Magazine* and by *Harper's Weekly*. His first novel, *Chita*, dealing with the tidal wave that wrought such havoc at Last Island, was published in *Harper's*, and in 1887 appeared the Oriental legends which he called *Chinese Ghosts*—one of the scarcest of his books, since nearly every copy was destroyed following a quarrel with his publisher.

While on a visit to New York in the spring of 1887 Hearn was introduced to Henry Mills Alden, editor of *Harper's*, who commissioned him to write articles on the West Indies. What a welcome task for this poor vagabond, out of harmony with his times, yearning for the warmth, the glamour, the indolence of the tropics! He returned in the autumn, but New York could no longer hold him, and he went back to the West Indies on the same boat that had brought him from those islands of enchantment. Perhaps the exotic, sensuous, unsophisticated women he had met and known and loved were the chief attraction to one who divided women into two classes—those of gentle birth, to whom he remained a revolting stranger, and the social and intellectual inferiors in whose company he felt no embarrassment.

A Lizard Basking in the July Sun

Life in Martinique was precarious in the extreme. While he revelled in the peace and sunshine of the island, like a lizard basking in the July sun, the absence of any regular market for his literary output meant that he was often without the means to support himself and obliged, therefore, to accept the charity of his coloured friends. The articles which *Harper's* accepted show that despite his pecuniary difficulties he was completely under the spell of the enchanting country and of its people. One has only to glance through the pages of *Two Years in the French West Indies* (1890), the book in which these articles were published, to realize the extent of his surrender to the magic of his surroundings. A quotation from *A Midsummer Trip to the Tropics* will give some indication of his feeling for beauty and colour:

'Morning. A gold sunrise over an indigo sea. The wind is a great warm caress; the sky is a spotless blue. We are steaming on Dominica. . . . While the silhouette is yet all violet in distance, nothing more solemnly beautiful can well be imagined: a vast cathedral shape, whose spires are mountain peaks, towering in the horizon, sheer up from the sea.
'We stay at Roseau only long enough to land the mails, and wonder at the loveliness of the island. A beautifully wrinkled mass of green and blue and gray;—a strangely abrupt peaking and heaping of the land. Behind the green heights loom the blues; behind these the grays —all pinnacled against the sky-glow—thrusting up through gaps or behind promontories. Indescribably exquisite the foldings and hollow-ings of the emerald coast. In glen and vale the color of cane-fields shines like a pooling of fluid bronze, as if the luminous essence of the

hill tints had been dripping down and clarifying there. Far to our
left, a bright green spur pierces into the now turquoise sea; and
beyond it, a beautiful mountain form, blue and curved like a hip,
slopes seaward, showing lighted wrinkles here and there, of
green. . . .'

Returning to New York in the spring of 1889, Lafcadio
Hearn left almost at once to visit Dr George Milbry
Gould at his home in Philadelphia. Two years earlier he
had been flattered to receive a letter from Gould warmly
praising one of his translations. Unaccustomed to having
his work commended, Hearn had been quick to send a
cordial reply, and an extensive correspondence soon
ripened into friendship. Gould, who was born in Maine in
1848, had been prevented by ill-health from pursuing his
training for the ministry. His illness apparently was due to
eyestrain, and after taking up medicine he preached the
gospel of the eyestrain origin of disease and mental
troubles. Many of his colleagues, however, unwilling to
subscribe to his rather sweeping statements, accused him
of promoting a fad. Gould did useful work in raising the
standard of contributions to the medical press. Possessing
a distinguished literary style, he edited the *Philadelphia
Medical Journal* and *American Medicine*, was author of the
fascinating *Biographic Clinics* and of *Anomalies and
Curiosities of Medicine*. As the compiler of a medical
dictionary which has been consulted by generations of
practitioners he was dubbed by one medical writer 'the
Johnson of Medical Lexicography'.

A mutual interest in literary expression enabled Hearn
and Gould to meet on common ground. For five months
Hearn remained under the hospitable roof of the ophthal-
mologist, who apparently conceived it his duty to bring
about his guest's reformation. He tried to influence him
to write works in which virtue triumphant was the central
theme. The only story which sprang from this source
but met with little success, was entitled *Karma*. Following
a misunderstanding over the disposition of his library—
at that time Gould seems to have had possession of everything that belonged to Hearn, except the clothes he wore—

the two men became bitter enemies, though Gould tried unsuccessfully to bring about a reconciliation. In 1908 Gould published a book, *Concerning Lafcadio Hearn*, in which he made what many considered an altogether unwarranted attack on Hearn's character and habits.

Lafcadio Hearn next made his way to New York, where he arrived in his usual state of impecuniosity. Setting his heart on going to Japan, and in order to raise the necessary funds, he sold several magazine articles for *Harper's* and performed the astonishing feat of translating Anatole France's *Le Crime de Sylvestre Bonnard* in a fortnight, the task bringing him in one hundred dollars.

Shortly after his arrival in Japan he wrote a most insulting letter to Harper's severing his connection with the firm. Hearn was at the time suffering more than ever from his customary persecution mania, in the clutches of which he imagined that Harper's were out to exploit his talents at starvation rates. This, of course, was pure delusion, and his hasty action left him once more without a livelihood. Fortunately, he obtained a post as teacher in a school at Matsue, a small town, in which many feudal customs survived and which afforded him a glimpse of a fast-disappearing Japan. His impressions were recorded in *Glimpses of Unfamiliar Japan* (1894).

One more Hearn's health threatened to give way. He was aged forty in the year of his arrival in Japan, and for much of his life he had suffered from overwork, privation, and diverse excesses. A wise fellow-teacher advised him to marry a young woman whose family, though poor, was of excellent character. Setsuko Koisumi was twenty-two years old, and Hearn settled down with his young wife to a life of domestic tranquillity. Matsue was very cold in the winter months, and the sun-worshipper who revelled in tropical heat, applied for a transfer and was moved to the Government College of Kumamoto. His first son was born in 1893. Legal considerations which would affect the status of his wife and son in the event of his death caused him to adopt Japanese nationality and to take the name of Koizumi Yakumo. In taking this step, however, he made a financial sacrifice, for his salary was immediately reduced from that paid to foreign teachers to the much lower native scale.

This incident created a bad impression on Hearn who, subject as he was to delusions of persecution, lost much of his former admiration and affection for the Japanese. In 1894, when he had been teaching at Kumamoto for three years, he resigned to take a position with the *Kobe Chronicle*. Finding newspaper work now too arduous for him, he secured the Chair of English Literature at the Imperial University of Tokio.

In his later years he became restless and dissatisfied, and attempted to obtain work in the United States. Invited to deliver a series of lectures at Cornell University, he was engaged in their preparation when the offer was withdrawn. When they appeared in book form in 1904 under the title *Japan: An Attempt at Interpretation*, they were found to have brilliantly achieved their object. In the previous books which he had produced at almost yearly intervals he had dealt with various facets of Japanese life. The last book presented a remarkable picture of Japan and the Japanese as a whole. Though he had never learned their language, he yet had a penetrating insight into the minds of the people with whom he had made his home. Hearn never saw the book in its final form, for on September 26, 1904, when he was enjoying the twilight on his veranda, he succumbed to a heart attack. Not long before he had instructed his eldest child: 'Put my bones in a jar worth about three sen and bury me in some temple on a hill.'

Under the Cherry Tree

Lafcadio Hearn came closer to finding happiness and peace in the land of cherry blossoms than anywhere else in the world. Among the Japanese, a nation of small men, his own small stature remained unnoticed, and he felt instantly at home. And his shyness was flattered when he was mistaken for a native. Yet absolute, serene tranquillity was never to be his lot. He lost his appointment at the University because he could not get on with his colleagues, whom he imagined to object to his atheism. It was his firm belief that 'being skeptical enables one to enjoy life better—to live like the ancients without the thought of the Shadow of Death. . . . I do not believe in God—neither God of Greece nor of Rome nor any other God. I do indeed revere Woman as the Creator, and I respect—yes, I almost believe in—the graceful Hellenic anthropomorphism which worshipped feminine softness and serpentine fascination and intoxicating loveliness in the garb of Venus Anadyomene.' He died a Buddhist: 'I am steeped in Buddhism, a Buddhism totally unlike that of books—something infinitely tender, touching, naïf, beautiful. I mingle with crowds of pilgrims to the great shrines; I ring the great bells; and burn incense rods before the great smiling gods.'

Lafcadio Hearn often worked his brain to the detriment of his body, believing that those in rude health seldom discerned the 'half lights'. At times he experimented on himself. In Cincinnati he attempted to alleviate the pangs of hunger by opium, and in Japan he tried to exist on a diet of rice and lotus roots. He was forced to the conclusion that these efforts to make the body a mere vehicle for the soul produced nervous irritability, weakened eyesight, and dyspepsia. When he wrote he sat at a high desk with paper and pen point about three inches from his eye, though his legible hand gave no indication that the mere act of writing was a physical labour. At times he would fall into an emotional trance, making him absentminded, when he would forget meals or to go to bed, and sometimes he would see ghostly apparitions or would hold communion with persons conjured up in his dreams.

Hearn's life could not be counted successful from worldly standards, but despite his physical handicaps he achieved the success which Walter Pater said was the only success in life, that which arises from the perception of beauty. With the curiously persistent power of genius he advanced, as he described it, 'to attain ideals beyond his reach, by the Divine Temptation of the Impossible'. 'Tis a far cry from a Greek tragedy centuries old, when from the white gleaming top of the Leucadian rock Sappho of Lesbos, in whose heart the rose of love had blossomed once so fragrantly, leaped into the fathomless sea, to a quiet cemetery in the land of bamboos and cherry trees. Here at fall of night a ghostly company of dragon flies fills the air, and on them, during the Feast of Lanterns, the dead return to the haunts of the quick. The air is filled, too, with the clear-throated song of a Japanese nightingale, a holy bird which they say professes Buddhism. Its song is a song of triumph, of the glory of life, the resurrection of the past, the exaltation of the present, the ecstasy of the future. And as it ascends into the empyrean, it makes the stars shine more brilliantly.

REFERENCES
and
Further Reading

REFERENCES

and

Further Reading

Thomas Carlyle

SIR J. CRICHTON-BROWNE: 'Carlyle—his wife and critics', *Journal of Mental Science*, 1898, **44,** 76–95.

SIR J. CRICHTON-BROWNE: 'Froude and Carlyle: the imputation considered medically', *British Medical Journal*, 1903, **i,** 1498–502.

SIR J. CRICHTON-BROWNE and A. CARLYLE: *The nemesis of Froude.* A rejoinder to J. A. Froude's 'My relations with Carlyle'. London: Lane. 1903.

JAMES L. HALLIDAY: *Mr. Carlyle, my patient.* London: William Heinemann. Medical, Books Ltd. 1949.

An ingenious, stimulating book, at times a little far-fetched. Too much psychological jargon for the layman.

Percy Bysshe Shelley

LEWIS J. MOORMAN: *Tuberculosis and Genius.* Chicago: University of Chicago Press. 1940, 192–234.

A. A. MOLL: 'Shelley the invalid,' *New York Medical Journal*, 1919, **110,** 934–41.

'The problem of Shelley's invalidism,' *Medical Press and Circular*, 1920, **N.S. 109,** 306.

H. ST. H. VERTUE: 'The tragedy of Shelley,' *Guy's Hospital Reports*, 1946, **95,** 53–72.

Walt Whitman

L. J. BRAGMAN: 'Walt Whitman, hospital attendant and medical critic,' *Medical Life*, 1932, **39,** 606–15.

J. C. TRENT: 'Walt Whitman—a case history,' *Surgery, Gynecology and Obstetrics*, 1948, **87,** 113–21.

Algernon Charles Swinburne

EDMUND GOSSE: *Life of Algernon Charles Swinburne.* London: Macmillan & Co. Ltd. 1917.

EDMUND GOSSE: Article on Swinburne in *Dictionary of National Biography*.

T. V. MOORE: 'A study in sadism: the life of Algernon Charles Swinburne', *Character and Personality*, 1937, **6,** 1–15.

L. J. BRAGMAN: 'The case of Algernon Charles Swinburne—a study in sadism', *Psychoanalytic Review*, 1934, **21,** 59–74.

Edgar Allan Poe

HERVEY ALLEN: *Israfel: the life and times of Edgar Allan Poe.* New York: Farrar & Rinehart, Inc. 1934.

MARIE BONAPARTE: *The life and works of Edgar Allan Poe: a psychoanalytic interpretation.* London: Imago Publishing Co. 1949.

L. PRUETTE: 'A psycho-analytical study of Edgar Allan Poe,' *American Journal of Psychology*, 1920, **31,** 370–402.

Charles Lamb

R. L. PITFIELD: 'A pitiful, ricketty, gasping, staggering, stuttering tom-fool,' *Annals of Medical History*, 1929, N.S. 1, 383–93.

E. V. LUCAS: *Life of Charles Lamb*. 2 Vols. London: Methuen. (Several editions.)

Thomas De Quincey

L. J. BRAGMAN: 'The medical wisdom of De Quincey', *Annals of Medical History*, 1928, 10, 451–9.

Confessions of an English Opium-Eater together with selections from the Autobiography of Thomas De Quincey. Edited and with an introduction by Edward Sackville-West. London: Cresset Press. 1950.

Charles Baudelaire

THÉOPHILE GAUTIER: *Charles Baudelaire: his life*. Translated into English, with selections from his poems, by Guy Thorne. London: Greening & Co. 1915.

HAROLD NICOLSON: 'Swinburne and Baudelaire', *Essays by Divers Hands*. London: Humphrey Milford, Oxford University Press. 1926, 117–37.

O. KUCERA: 'The mechanisms of regression in the poetry of Baudelaire and his followers', *International Journal of Psycho-Analysis*, 1950, 31, 98–102.

Honoré De Balzac

A. TRILLAT: 'Sur les médecins dans la "Comédie Humaine" d'Honoré Balzac', *Bulletin de l'Académie de Médecine*, 1939, **121,** 200–7.

Aesculape, March, 1951, **32,** 49–71. (Balzac number.)

STEFAN ZWEIG: *Balzac*. Translated by William and Dorothy Rose. London: Cassell. 1947.

John Keats

SIR GEORGE NEWMAN: 'John Keats: apothecary and poet', *Interpreters of Nature*. London: Faber and Gwyer. 1927, 161–92.

SIR WILLIAM HALE-WHITE: *Keats as Doctor and Patient*. London: Oxford University Press. 1938.

LEWIS J. MOORMAN: *Tuberculosis and Genius*. Chicago: University of Chicago Press. 1940, 235–58.

R. L. PITFIELD: 'John Keats—the reactions of a genius to tuberculosis and other adversities', *Annals of Medical History*, 1930, **N.S. 2,** 530–46.

E. W. GOODALL: 'Some examples of the knowledge of medicine exhibited in the poems of John Keats', *Guy's Hospital Gazette*, 1936, **50,** 238–40.

SIR ROBERT ARMSTRONG-JONES: 'The poet Keats' trip to Scotland, July, 1818', *Annals of Medical History*, 1937, **N.S. 9,** 101–10.

SIR ROBERT ARMSTRONG-JONES: 'Some remarks on Keats and his friends', *Annals of Medical History*, 1938, **N.S. 10,** 433–44.

Robert Burns

SIR JAMES CRICHTON-BROWNE: *Burns from a new point of view*. London: William Hodge & Co. Ltd. 1937.

DE LANCEY FERGUSON: *Pride and passion: Robert Burns*. New York: Oxford University Press. 1939.

H. B. ANDERSON: 'Robert Burns, his medical friends, attendants and biographer', *Annals of Medical History*, 1928, **10,** 47–58.

S. W. SMITH: 'The disease that killed Robert Burns', *British Medical Journal*, 1944, **ii,** 864.

Lord Byron

E. B. KRUMBHAAR: 'The post-mortem examination of Lord Byron's body', *Annals of Medical History*, 1923, **5,** 283–4.

C. A. WOOD: 'Julius Millingen, Lord Byron's physician', *Annals of Medical History*, 1929, **N.S. 1,** 260–9.

JAMES KEMBLE: *Idols and Invalids*. London: Methuen & Co. Ltd. (Fountain Library). 1935, 1–26.

Alexander Pope

A. POPE: *Works*. New Edition . . . with introduction and notes by W. Elwin and W. J. Courthope. London: John Murray. 10 Vols. 1871–89.

IRIS BARRY: *Portrait of Lady Mary Wortley Montagu*. London: Ernest Benn, Ltd. 1928.

Lafcadio Hearn

G. M. GOULD: *Concerning Lafcadio Hearn*. London: T. Fisher Unwin. 1908.

Dictionary of American Biography, Vol. 8. London: Humphrey Milford, Oxford University Press. 1932.

INDEX